Water Resource Measurements

A Handbook for
Hydrologists and Engineers

Bruce P. Van Haveren

OCLC #132919731   3/27/95

FOUNDED
1881

American Water Works Association

Copyright ©1986
American Water Works Association
6666 West Quincy Avenue
Denver, CO 80235

Printed in USA

ISBN 0-89867-345-3

Contents

Preface

This handbook has been assembled primarily for the practicing hydrologist, water engineer, planner, and field technician. It has been designed to function as both a field and office reference.

In more than 17 years as a technician and hydrologist, I have often wished for a single, concise handbook of formulas and conversion tables that I could throw into my briefcase or rucksack. Unfortunately, no such handbook has been available until now.

From numerous field assignments and data analysis projects I have accumulated a notebook of useful water conversion factors, hydraulic tables, and other related technical aids. This handbook was the logical outcome.

I have strived through several reviews and reference crosschecks to eliminate all possible errors. If any are found I would appreciate being notified through the publisher. I also welcome suggestions for new material for future editions.

Acknowledgments

This book was not an individual effort by any means. I want to recognize my many hydrology colleagues who, over the years, provided me with ideas for material. Shirley McCulloch and Herman Weiss were responsible for the illustrations. John Rieman and his staff at AWWA patiently and professionally guided the book through the publication process. Lastly, I owe much thanks to my family for putting up with me when I occasionally borrowed "family time" to complete this project.

—*Bruce P. Van Haveren*

The American Water Works Association would like to acknowledge the contributions of the following reviewers: Thomas J. Buchanan, Assistant Chief Hydrologist for Operations, US Department of the Interior, Geological Survey, Reston, Va.; Norman A. Evans, Director, Colorado Water Resources Research Institute, Colorado State University, Fort Collins, Colo.; Laurent McReynolds, Engineer in Charge, Water Quality Division, Department of Water and Power, The City of Los Angeles, Los Angeles, Calif.; and Paul V. Roberts, Associate Professor of Environmental Engineering, Department of Civil Engineering, Stanford University, Stanford, Calif. The time and effort these individuals contributed to the review of the material presented in this book is greatly appreciated.

Introduction

This book deals primarily with numbers, especially as they are used in the systematic process of scientific data collection, analysis, and interpretation. Numbers are often abused, even by experienced scientists. The following discussion serves as a review to remind the reader of the basic principles of working with numerical data.

Accuracy and Precision of Numbers in Data Collection

The meaning of accuracy, precision, and related terms are sometimes not clearly defined. Before discussing the sources and nature of errors in the data collection and analysis process, some definitions are presented in Table I.1 to ensure an understanding of the succeeding material. The distinction between accuracy and precision, a common source of confusion, is portrayed graphically in Figure I.1.

The scientist or technician must always be aware of potential errors in collecting and handling data. These errors can be either random or systematic. Bias and decreased accuracy result from systematic errors. Random errors lead to decreased precision and loss of accuracy. Most errors result from faulty equipment, incorrect sampling or measurement procedures, observer mistakes, weather and other external effects on equipment, and faulty recording of data.

In nearly all data collection activities, the number resulting from or representing a measurement is an estimate of the true, but usually unknown, value. There are exceptions to this rule, such as when a whole number results from a tally. In hydrology, we nearly always deal with measurements that are estimates of the true value. For example, assume you are measuring the water level in a lake. If you take a single measurement of water level using an instrument having a resolution of ± 0.001 ft and obtain a measurement of 580.613, the last digit, 3, is considered significant and its place to the right of the decimal indicates a certain level of precision of that measurement. In this case the indicated precision corresponds to the given resolution of the instrument. This value is not likely to be the true water level, but it represents an estimate within the established precision of the true value.

The last digit of a number representing a scientific measurement should always be significant. If a zero appears as the last digit, it is presumed significant. This does not mean that the last digit is necessarily correct, but that it represents the most probable value within the limits of the stated or implied precision.

Table I.1   Terminology of Data Collection and Analysis

Term	Definition
Accuracy	The closeness of a measurement to the true value of the quantity being measured or to an accepted reference value.
Bias	A systematic variation or lack of randomness in a set of observations that results from a systematic error in data collection or analysis.
Confidence level	A quantitative expression of the reliability of an estimated value. The expression is usually stated in probability terms.
Consistency	A property of numbers that is related to sample size. As sample size increases, a consistent sample does not deviate from the population mean more or less than a fixed amount. An unbiased sample is consistent but a consistent sample is not necessarily unbiased.
Efficiency	A measure of the quality of an estimator or set of observations. Efficiency is inversely proportional to the variance. A sample is more efficient if it has a smaller variance than another sample.
Implied precision	The precision, implied by the position of the decimal point, of a number having no predetermined or stated precision.
Nominal value	A reference, designated, or theoretical value that may vary from the actual value.
Precision	The variation in an observation or set of observations due to random error. It is the measure of the repeatability of a series of observations or measurements.
Random error	Chance fluctuations in the value of a variable that occur when a series of measurements are taken under the exact same conditions.
Reliability	The expression of how well a model or other predictor technique measures what it is supposed to measure, including both accuracy and precision properties. Refers also to the consistency and precision of an instrument or measurement technique.
Repeatability	The precision associated with an individual observer taking several measurements of the same variable under the same conditions but at different times using the same equipment or measurement technique.
Reproducibility	The precision associated with more than one observer taking separate measurements of the same variable under the same conditions using the same or different equipment or measurement techniques, or the precision associated with an observer taking measurements of the same variable under the same conditions using different equipment or procedures.
Resolution	The capability of distinguishing between consecutive units of measurement on an instrument or chart scale or between signals from a data collection device.
Sensitivity	The ability of an instrument (or instrument plus observer) to measure changes in a variable or the ability of a model or other mathematical predictor to produce realistic responses in output variables when levels of input variables are changed.
Significance	In data analysis, significance refers to the relationship of a number to some base datum or reference value. In statistical analyses the term should be qualified with a probability statement.
Sufficiency	The degree to which a parameter derived from a given sample represents or extracts information from the corresponding population.
Systematic error	Constant or systematic departures in the values of a variable that occur when a series of measurements are taken under the exact same conditions.

Table I.1   Terminology of Data Collection and Analysis (continued)

Term	Definition
Tolerance	The allowable deviation from a numerical standard or the range of variation permitted a given number.
Traceability	In equipment calibration, the ability of an instrument to produce results of an accuracy and precision relative to some national or other specified standard.
Uncertainty	The variation of a random variable or the tendency of outcomes to vary when repeated measurements are made under identical conditions. Uncertainty consists of both random and systematic error.
Validity	The confidence value one places on an observation, measurement, analysis, conclusion, or interpretation with respect to either precision or accuracy.

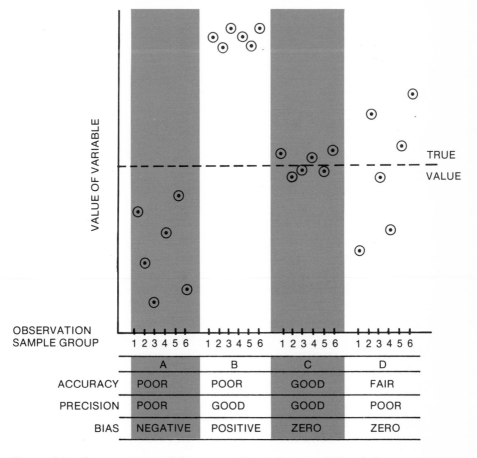

Figure I.1   Comparison of Accuracy, Precision, and Bias (after McCuen, 1979)

Assuming that bias is absent, a number becomes more accurate as more significant digits are added to the right of the decimal. Implied precision or implied limits refers to the unstated tolerance of a number. For example, the number 44 has implied limits of 43.5 and 44.5. The lake level measurement of 580.613 has implied limits of 580.6125 and 580.6135.

Guidelines for Converting Numerical Data

Converting numbers from one unit system to another is unavoidable when working with hydrologic data. In converting from one unit system to another, establishing a procedure for determining how many decimal positions are to be retained can be difficult. Retaining too many decimal positions results in an overextension of precision; dropping significant digits results in a loss of accuracy. The intended precision is established either with stated tolerance limits or based on knowledge of the original measurement.

If rounding is either necessary or desirable, the following procedure should be used:

When the digit to be dropped is:	The last digit retained is:	Examples
<5	unchanged	2.44 = 2.4
>5	increased by 1	2.46 = 2.5
5, followed by 0 or a blank	unchanged if even,	2.45 = 2.4
	increased by 1 if odd	2.55 = 2.6
5, followed by non-zero	increased by 1	2.453 = 2.5

The conversion process can be summarized by the following four steps:

1. Determine the implied precision based on
   a. knowledge of the original measurement, or
   b. plus and minus one-half the least significant digit;
   c. the conversion constant should contain at least the same number of significant digits as are contained in the original value.
2. Convert the dimension and the implied precision using the appropriate conversion factor. Do not round either the conversion factor or the original value before the arithmetic operation is performed; accuracy will be lost if the rounding process is performed prematurely.
3. Select the smallest number of significant digits to the right of the decimal necessary to reflect the required precision as determined in 1. As a general rule, the multiplicand or dividend should have the same precision as the least precise number involved in the conversion.
4. Round the converted number to the specified number of decimal positions in accordance with the rounding rules previously discussed.

For arithmetic operations involving numbers of the same units but different levels of precision, the following rules apply:

1. For addition and subtraction, the answer shall contain no more significant digits following the decimal than are contained in the least precise number. Numbers other than the least precise number should be rounded to have one more significant digit than the least precise number.
2. For multiplication and division, the product or dividend shall not contain any more significant digits than are contained in the least precise number. Do not use preliminary rounding.

Conceptual Guide to Planning and Conducting Water Resource Investigations

Planning a scientific investigation to answer specific resource management questions is an intellectual activity. Thinking about the data you are going to collect, why these data are needed, and what you are going to do with the results are mental activities prerequisite to both problem solving and project planning.

There are obvious advantages to developing and following a logical approach to resource management investigations. Back-tracking, wheel-spinning, and repeat efforts are avoided. You stand a better chance of getting management and peer support. You are on firmer ground if the project results are scrutinized in legal proceedings.

The following outline can be used for a variety of purposes ranging from a quick field investigation to a complex and long-term research project; the thought process is the same.

A. Identify and Define the Problem
  1. What are the issues?
  2. What are the policies of the organization with respect to each issue?
  3. Are there management goals in effect for the area of interest?
  4. What is the problem to be solved?
  5. Is the problem real?
  6. Who has the problem?
  7. Describe the symptoms of the problem.
  8. If measurable, quantify the problem in terms of its direct effects.
  9. Define the problem from a scientific perspective.
  10. Define the problem from management's perspective.
B. Analyze the Problem
  1. What is already known about the problem?
  2. Determine the causes (not the symptoms) of the problem. If not immediately discernible, design and conduct a specific investigation to determine the causes.
  3. Is the problem treatable?
  4. Can the problem be treated with available resources?

C. State Clear Objectives
1. What are the specific questions to be answered?
2. Is the problem to be solved by research or through routine data collection?
3. What data variables must be addressed?
4. Quantify the objectives and specify "what, where, and when."

D. Design the Investigation
1. Keep the objectives clearly in mind.
2. Analyze past experience.
3. Determine budget and time constraints.
4. Select an overall strategy for data collection and analysis.
5. Identify and define the potential sources of error.
6. How many stations, samples, and replications will be needed?
7. Choose the desired accuracy and precision limits for data collection and analysis.
8. Select the probability level for statistical analysis.
9. State hypotheses and determine how they will be tested.
10. Establish a realistic timetable for the project.
11. Identify field sites, equipment, and personnel needed.
12. Determine and document methods of data collection, analysis, storage, and retrieval.

E. Conduct the Investigation
1. Keep objectives clearly in mind.
2. Prepare an action plan before going to the field; include equipment lists and personnel duties.
3. Maintain a diary of places, events, people involved, and environmental factors.
4. Note any departures from the established study design.

F. Analyze All Data Collected
1. Keep objectives clearly in mind.
2. Use proper computational methods.
3. Leave a trail others can follow.
4. Draw inferences based on statistical tests, but recognize the limitations of such tests.
5. Review progress and objectives often enough to ensure attainment of objectives.
6. If changes to study procedures must be made, make them consciously and modify work plan accordingly with formal documentation of each change.

G. Interpret Results
1. Keep objectives clearly in mind.

2. Who is the intended audience?
3. Are the interpretations supported by the data?
4. Do the results agree with reality?

H. Prepare Necessary Reports
   1. Keep report objectives clearly in mind. At least one report must satisfy the original objectives of the investigation.
   2. Different audiences require different reports.
   3. Allow sufficient time and funds for preparation of reports.
   4. Arrange for formal publication in appropriate outlets—you have a professional responsibility to inform all possible interest groups.

I. Terminate the Investigation on Schedule
   1. Do not fall into the "one more year of data" trap.
   2. Inform all interested parties of project termination.
   3. Close out all project files and arrange for appropriate archiving.

1

Mathematical Equivalents
and Tables

1.1 Definitions ⎯⎯⎯⎯⎯⎯⎯⎯⎯⎯⎯⎯⎯⎯⎯⎯⎯⎯⎯⎯⎯⎯⎯⎯⎯⎯⎯⎯⎯

Mathematical Constants

π = 3.141 592 653 589 793 238 46

e = 2.718 281 828 459 045 235 36

1.2 Square Roots of Numbers*

	0.000	0.001	0.002	0.003	0.004	0.005	0.006	0.007	0.008	0.009
0.00	0.000	0.032	0.045	0.055	0.063	0.071	0.077	0.084	0.089	0.095
0.01	0.100	0.105	0.110	0.114	0.118	0.122	0.126	0.130	0.134	0.138
0.02	0.141	0.145	0.148	0.152	0.155	0.158	0.161	0.164	0.167	0.170
0.03	0.173	0.176	0.179	0.182	0.184	0.187	0.190	0.192	0.195	0.197
0.04	0.200	0.202	0.205	0.207	0.210	0.212	0.214	0.217	0.219	0.221
0.05	0.224	0.226	0.228	0.230	0.232	0.235	0.237	0.239	0.241	0.243
0.06	0.245	0.247	0.249	0.251	0.253	0.255	0.257	0.259	0.261	0.263
0.07	0.265	0.266	0.268	0.270	0.272	0.274	0.276	0.277	0.279	0.281
0.08	0.283	0.285	0.286	0.288	0.290	0.292	0.293	0.295	0.297	0.298
0.09	0.300	0.302	0.303	0.305	0.307	0.308	0.310	0.311	0.313	0.315
0.10	0.316	0.318	0.319	0.321	0.322	0.324	0.326	0.327	0.329	0.330

*Useful for computations of $S^{1/2}$ in the Manning equation.

1.3   Decimal Equivalents of Fractions

Fraction	Decimal	Fraction	Decimal
$1/64$	0.01563	$33/64$	0.51563
$1/32$	0.03125	$17/32$	0.53125
$3/64$	0.04688	$35/64$	0.54688
$1/16$	0.06250	$9/16$	0.56250
$5/64$	0.07813	$37/64$	0.57813
$3/32$	0.09375	$19/32$	0.59375
$7/64$	0.10938	$39/64$	0.60938
$1/8$	0.12500	$5/8$	0.62500
$9/64$	0.14063	$41/64$	0.64063
$5/32$	0.15625	$21/32$	0.65625
$11/64$	0.17188	$43/64$	0.67188
$3/16$	0.18750	$11/16$	0.68750
$13/64$	0.20313	$45/64$	0.70313
$7/32$	0.21875	$23/32$	0.71875
$15/64$	0.23438	$47/64$	0.73438
$1/4$	0.25000	$3/4$	0.75000
$17/64$	0.26563	$49/64$	0.76563
$9/32$	0.28125	$25/32$	0.78125
$19/64$	0.29688	$51/64$	0.79688
$10/32$	0.31250	$13/16$	0.81250
$21/64$	0.32813	$53/64$	0.82813
$11/32$	0.34375	$27/32$	0.84375
$23/64$	0.35938	$55/64$	0.85938
$3/8$	0.37500	$7/8$	0.87500
$25/64$	0.39063	$57/64$	0.89063
$13/32$	0.40625	$29/32$	0.90625
$27/64$	0.42188	$59/64$	0.92188
$7/16$	0.43750	$15/16$	0.93750
$29/64$	0.45313	$61/64$	0.95313
$15/32$	0.46875	$31/32$	0.96875
$31/64$	0.48438	$63/64$	0.98438
$1/2$	0.50000		

1.4 Two-thirds Powers of Numbers*

	0.0	0.1	0.2	0.3	0.4	0.5	0.6	0.7	0.8	0.9
0	0.00	0.22	0.34	0.45	0.54	0.63	0.71	0.79	0.86	0.93
1	1.00	1.07	1.13	1.19	1.25	1.31	1.37	1.42	1.48	1.53
2	1.59	1.64	1.69	1.74	1.79	1.84	1.89	1.94	1.99	2.03
3	2.08	2.13	2.17	2.22	2.26	2.31	2.35	2.39	2.44	2.48
4	2.52	2.56	2.60	2.64	2.69	2.73	2.77	2.81	2.85	2.88
5	2.92	2.96	3.00	3.04	3.08	3.12	3.15	3.19	3.23	3.27
6	3.30	3.34	3.37	3.41	3.45	3.48	3.52	3.55	3.59	3.62
7	3.66	3.69	3.73	3.76	3.80	3.83	3.87	3.90	3.93	3.97
8	4.00	4.03	4.07	4.10	4.13	4.16	4.20	4.23	4.26	4.29
9	4.33	4.36	4.39	4.42	4.45	4.49	4.52	4.55	4.58	4.61
10	4.64	4.67	4.70	4.73	4.76	4.80	4.83	4.86	4.89	4.92
11	4.95	4.98	5.01	5.04	5.07	5.09	5.12	5.15	5.18	5.21
12	5.24	5.27	5.30	5.33	5.36	5.39	5.41	5.44	5.47	5.50
13	5.53	5.56	5.59	5.61	5.64	5.67	5.70	5.73	5.75	5.78
14	5.81	5.84	5.86	5.89	5.92	5.95	5.97	6.00	6.03	6.06
15	6.08	6.11	6.14	6.16	6.19	6.22	6.24	6.27	6.30	6.32
16	6.35	6.38	6.40	6.43	6.45	6.48	6.51	6.53	6.56	6.59
17	6.61	6.64	6.66	6.69	6.71	6.74	6.77	6.79	6.82	6.84
18	6.87	6.89	6.92	6.94	6.97	6.99	7.02	7.05	7.07	7.10
19	7.12	7.15	7.17	7.20	7.22	7.24	7.27	7.29	7.32	7.34
20	7.37	7.39	7.42	7.44	7.47	7.49	7.51	7.54	7.56	7.59
21	7.61	7.64	7.66	7.68	7.71	7.73	7.76	7.78	7.80	7.83
22	7.85	7.88	7.90	7.92	7.95	7.97	7.99	8.02	8.04	8.06
23	8.09	8.11	8.13	8.16	8.18	8.20	8.23	8.25	8.27	8.30
24	8.32	8.34	8.37	8.39	8.41	8.44	8.46	8.48	8.50	8.53
25	8.55	8.57	8.60	8.62	8.64	8.66	8.69	8.71	8.73	8.75
26	8.78	8.80	8.82	8.84	8.87	8.89	8.91	8.93	8.96	8.98
27	9.00	9.02	9.04	9.07	9.09	9.11	9.13	9.15	9.18	9.20
28	9.22	9.24	9.26	9.29	9.31	9.33	9.35	9.37	9.40	9.42
29	9.44	9.46	9.48	9.50	9.53	9.55	9.57	9.59	9.61	9.63
30	9.65	9.68	9.70	9.72	9.74	9.76	9.78	9.80	9.83	9.85
31	9.87	9.89	9.91	9.93	9.95	9.97	10.00	10.02	10.04	10.06
32	10.08	10.10	10.12	10.14	10.16	10.18	10.20	10.23	10.25	10.27
33	10.29	10.31	10.33	10.35	10.37	10.39	10.41	10.43	10.45	10.47
34	10.50	10.52	10.54	10.56	10.58	10.60	10.62	10.64	10.66	10.68
35	10.70	10.72	10.74	10.76	10.78	10.80	10.82	10.84	10.86	10.88
36	10.90	10.92	10.94	10.96	10.98	11.00	11.02	11.04	11.06	11.08
37	11.10	11.12	11.14	11.16	11.18	11.20	11.22	11.24	11.26	11.28
38	11.30	11.32	11.34	11.36	11.38	11.40	11.42	11.44	11.46	11.48
39	11.50	11.52	11.54	11.56	11.58	11.60	11.62	11.64	11.66	11.68
40	11.70	11.72	11.74	11.75	11.77	11.79	11.81	11.83	11.85	11.87
41	11.89	11.91	11.93	11.95	11.97	11.99	12.01	12.03	12.04	12.06
42	12.08	12.10	12.12	12.14	12.16	12.18	12.20	12.22	12.24	12.25
43	12.27	12.29	12.31	12.33	12.35	12.37	12.39	12.41	12.43	12.44
44	12.46	12.48	12.50	12.52	12.54	12.56	12.58	12.60	12.61	12.63
45	12.65	12.67	12.69	12.71	12.73	12.75	12.76	12.78	12.80	12.82
46	12.84	12.86	12.88	12.89	12.91	12.93	12.95	12.97	12.99	13.01
47	13.02	13.04	13.06	13.08	13.10	13.12	13.13	13.15	13.17	13.19
48	13.21	13.23	13.24	13.26	13.28	13.30	13.32	13.34	13.35	13.37
49	13.39	13.41	13.43	13.45	13.46	13.48	13.50	13.52	13.54	13.55
50	13.57	13.59	13.61	13.63	13.64	13.66	13.68	13.70	13.72	13.73

*Useful for computations of $R^{2/3}$ in the Manning equation.

1.4 Two-thirds Powers of Numbers (continued)*

	0.0	0.1	0.2	0.3	0.4	0.5	0.6	0.7	0.8	0.9
51	13.75	13.77	13.79	13.81	13.82	13.84	13.86	13.88	13.90	13.91
52	13.93	13.95	13.97	13.99	14.00	14.02	14.04	14.06	14.07	14.09
53	14.11	14.13	14.15	14.16	14.18	14.20	14.22	14.23	14.25	14.27
54	14.29	14.30	14.32	14.34	14.36	14.37	14.39	14.41	14.43	14.44
55	14.46	14.48	14.50	14.51	14.53	14.55	14.57	14.58	14.60	14.62
56	14.64	14.65	14.67	14.69	14.71	14.72	14.74	14.76	14.78	14.79
57	14.81	14.83	14.85	14.86	14.88	14.90	14.91	14.93	14.95	14.97
58	14.98	15.00	15.02	15.04	15.05	15.07	15.09	15.10	15.12	15.14
59	15.16	15.17	15.19	15.21	15.22	15.24	15.26	15.28	15.29	15.31
60	15.33	15.34	15.36	15.38	15.39	15.41	15.43	15.45	15.46	15.48
61	15.50	15.51	15.53	15.55	15.56	15.58	15.60	15.61	15.63	15.65
62	15.66	15.68	15.70	15.72	15.73	15.75	15.77	15.78	15.80	15.82
63	15.83	15.85	15.87	15.88	15.90	15.92	15.93	15.95	15.97	15.98
64	16.00	16.02	16.03	16.05	16.07	16.08	16.10	16.12	16.13	16.15
65	16.17	16.18	16.20	16.22	16.23	16.25	16.27	16.28	16.30	16.32
66	16.33	16.35	16.36	16.38	16.40	16.41	16.43	16.45	16.46	16.48
67	16.50	16.51	16.53	16.55	16.56	16.58	16.59	16.61	16.63	16.64
68	16.66	16.68	16.69	16.71	16.73	16.74	16.76	16.77	16.79	16.81
69	16.82	16.84	16.86	16.87	16.89	16.90	16.92	16.94	16.95	16.97
70	16.98	17.00	17.02	17.03	17.05	17.07	17.08	17.10	17.11	17.13
71	17.15	17.16	17.18	17.19	17.21	17.23	17.24	17.26	17.27	17.29
72	17.31	17.32	17.34	17.36	17.37	17.39	17.40	17.42	17.43	17.45
73	17.47	17.48	17.50	17.51	17.53	17.55	17.56	17.58	17.59	17.61
74	17.63	17.64	17.66	17.67	17.69	17.71	17.72	17.74	17.75	17.77
75	17.78	17.80	17.82	17.83	17.85	17.86	17.88	17.89	17.91	17.93
76	17.94	17.96	17.97	17.99	18.01	18.02	18.04	18.05	18.07	18.08
77	18.10	18.11	18.13	18.15	18.16	18.18	18.19	18.21	18.22	18.24
78	18.26	18.27	18.29	18.30	18.32	18.33	18.35	18.36	18.38	18.40
79	18.41	18.43	18.44	18.46	18.47	18.49	18.50	18.52	18.54	18.55
80	18.57	18.58	18.60	18.61	18.63	18.64	18.66	18.67	18.69	18.71
81	18.72	18.74	18.75	18.77	18.78	18.80	18.81	18.83	18.84	18.86
82	18.87	18.89	18.91	18.92	18.94	18.95	18.97	18.98	19.00	19.01
83	19.03	19.04	19.06	19.07	19.09	19.10	19.12	19.13	19.15	19.16
84	19.18	19.20	19.21	19.23	19.24	19.26	19.27	19.29	19.30	19.32
85	19.33	19.35	19.36	19.38	19.39	19.41	19.42	19.44	19.45	19.47
86	19.48	19.50	19.51	19.53	19.54	19.56	19.57	19.59	19.60	19.62
87	19.63	19.65	19.66	19.68	19.69	19.71	19.72	19.74	19.75	19.77
88	19.78	19.80	19.81	19.83	19.84	19.86	19.87	19.89	19.90	19.92
89	19.93	19.95	19.96	19.98	19.99	20.01	20.02	20.04	20.05	20.07
90	20.08	20.10	20.11	20.13	20.14	20.16	20.17	20.19	20.20	20.22
91	20.23	20.25	20.26	20.28	20.29	20.31	20.32	20.34	20.35	20.36
92	20.38	20.39	20.41	20.42	20.44	20.45	20.47	20.48	20.50	20.51
93	20.53	20.54	20.56	20.57	20.59	20.60	20.62	20.63	20.64	20.66
94	20.67	20.69	20.70	20.72	20.73	20.75	20.76	20.78	20.79	20.81
95	20.82	20.83	20.85	20.86	20.88	20.89	20.91	20.92	20.94	20.95
96	20.97	20.98	21.00	21.01	21.02	21.04	21.05	21.07	21.08	21.10
97	21.11	21.13	21.14	21.15	21.17	21.18	21.20	21.21	21.23	21.24
98	21.26	21.27	21.29	21.30	21.31	21.33	21.34	21.36	21.37	21.39
99	21.40	21.41	21.43	21.44	21.46	21.47	21.49	21.50	21.52	21.53
100	21.54	21.56	21.57	21.59	21.60	21.62	21.63	21.64	21.66	21.67

*Useful for computations of $R^{2/3}$ in the Manning equation.

1.5 Three-halves Powers of Numbers*

	0.00	0.01	0.02	0.03	0.04	0.05	0.06	0.07	0.08	0.09
0.0	0.000	0.001	0.003	0.005	0.008	0.011	0.015	0.019	0.023	0.027
0.1	0.032	0.036	0.042	0.047	0.052	0.058	0.064	0.070	0.076	0.083
0.2	0.089	0.096	0.103	0.110	0.118	0.125	0.133	0.140	0.148	0.156
0.3	0.164	0.173	0.181	0.190	0.198	0.207	0.216	0.225	0.234	0.244
0.4	0.253	0.263	0.272	0.282	0.292	0.302	0.312	0.322	0.333	0.343
0.5	0.354	0.364	0.375	0.386	0.397	0.408	0.419	0.430	0.442	0.453
0.6	0.465	0.476	0.488	0.500	0.512	0.524	0.536	0.548	0.561	0.573
0.7	0.586	0.598	0.611	0.624	0.637	0.650	0.663	0.676	0.689	0.702
0.8	0.716	0.729	0.743	0.756	0.770	0.784	0.798	0.811	0.826	0.840
0.9	0.854	0.868	0.882	0.897	0.911	0.926	0.941	0.955	0.970	0.985
1.0	1.000	1.015	1.030	1.045	1.061	1.076	1.091	1.107	1.122	1.138
1.1	1.154	1.169	1.185	1.201	1.217	1.233	1.249	1.266	1.282	1.298
1.2	1.315	1.331	1.348	1.364	1.381	1.398	1.414	1.431	1.448	1.465
1.3	1.482	1.499	1.517	1.534	1.551	1.569	1.586	1.604	1.621	1.639
1.4	1.657	1.674	1.692	1.710	1.728	1.746	1.764	1.782	1.800	1.819
1.5	1.837	1.856	1.874	1.893	1.911	1.930	1.948	1.967	1.986	2.005
1.6	2.024	2.043	2.062	2.081	2.100	2.119	2.139	2.158	2.178	2.197
1.7	2.217	2.236	2.256	2.275	2.295	2.315	2.335	2.355	2.375	2.395
1.8	2.415	2.435	2.455	2.476	2.496	2.516	2.537	2.557	2.578	2.598
1.9	2.619	2.640	2.660	2.681	2.702	2.723	2.744	2.765	2.786	2.807
2.0	2.828	2.850	2.871	2.892	2.914	2.935	2.957	2.978	3.000	3.021
2.1	3.043	3.065	3.087	3.109	3.131	3.153	3.175	3.197	3.219	3.241
2.2	3.263	3.285	3.308	3.330	3.353	3.375	3.398	3.420	3.443	3.465
2.3	3.488	3.511	3.534	3.557	3.580	3.602	3.626	3.649	3.672	3.695
2.4	3.718	3.741	3.765	3.788	3.811	3.835	3.858	3.882	3.906	3.929
2.5	3.953	3.977	4.000	4.024	4.048	4.072	4.096	4.120	4.144	4.168
2.6	4.192	4.217	4.241	4.265	4.289	4.314	4.338	4.363	4.387	4.412
2.7	4.437	4.461	4.486	4.511	4.536	4.560	4.585	4.610	4.635	4.660
2.8	4.685	4.710	4.736	4.761	4.786	4.811	4.837	4.862	4.888	4.913
2.9	4.939	4.964	4.990	5.015	5.041	5.067	5.093	5.118	5.144	5.170
3.0	5.196	5.222	5.248	5.274	5.300	5.327	5.353	5.379	5.405	5.432
3.1	5.458	5.485	5.511	5.538	5.564	5.591	5.617	5.644	5.671	5.698
3.2	5.724	5.751	5.778	5.805	5.832	5.859	5.886	5.913	5.940	5.968
3.3	5.995	6.022	6.049	6.077	6.104	6.132	6.159	6.186	6.214	6.242
3.4	6.269	6.297	6.325	6.352	6.380	6.408	6.436	6.464	6.492	6.520
3.5	6.548	6.576	6.604	6.632	6.660	6.689	6.717	6.745	6.774	6.802
3.6	6.831	6.859	6.888	6.916	6.945	6.973	7.002	7.031	7.059	7.088
3.7	7.117	7.146	7.175	7.204	7.233	7.262	7.291	7.320	7.349	7.378
3.8	7.408	7.437	7.466	7.495	7.525	7.554	7.584	7.613	7.643	7.672
3.9	7.702	7.732	7.761	7.791	7.821	7.850	7.880	7.910	7.940	7.970
4.0	8.000	8.030	8.060	8.090	8.120	8.150	8.181	8.211	8.241	8.272
4.1	8.302	8.332	8.363	8.393	8.424	8.454	8.485	8.515	8.546	8.577
4.2	8.607	8.638	8.669	8.700	8.731	8.762	8.793	8.824	8.855	8.886
4.3	8.917	8.948	8.979	9.010	9.041	9.073	9.104	9.135	9.167	9.198
4.4	9.230	9.261	9.293	9.324	9.356	9.387	9.419	9.451	9.482	9.514
4.5	9.546	9.578	9.610	9.642	9.674	9.705	9.737	9.770	9.802	9.834
4.6	9.866	9.898	9.930	9.963	9.995	10.027	10.060	10.092	10.124	10.157
4.7	10.189	10.222	10.254	10.287	10.320	10.352	10.385	10.418	10.451	10.483
4.8	10.516	10.549	10.582	10.615	10.648	10.681	10.714	10.747	10.780	10.813
4.9	10.847	10.880	10.913	10.946	10.980	11.013	11.046	11.080	11.113	11.147
5.0	11.180	11.214	11.247	11.281	11.315	11.348	11.382	11.416	11.450	11.484

*Useful for hydraulic head computations.

1.5 Three-halves Powers of Numbers (continued)*

	0.00	0.01	0.02	0.03	0.04	0.05	0.06	0.07	0.08	0.09
5.1	11.517	11.551	11.585	11.619	11.653	11.687	11.721	11.755	11.789	11.824
5.2	11.858	11.892	11.926	11.961	11.995	12.029	12.064	12.098	12.133	12.167
5.3	12.202	12.236	12.271	12.305	12.340	12.375	12.409	12.444	12.479	12.514
5.4	12.548	12.583	12.618	12.653	12.688	12.723	12.758	12.793	12.828	12.863
5.5	12.899	12.934	12.969	13.004	13.040	13.075	13.110	13.146	13.181	13.217
5.6	13.252	13.288	13.323	13.359	13.394	13.430	13.466	13.501	13.537	13.573
5.7	13.609	13.644	13.680	13.716	13.752	13.788	13.824	13.860	13.896	13.932
5.8	13.968	14.004	14.041	14.077	14.113	14.149	14.186	14.222	14.258	14.295
5.9	14.331	14.368	14.404	14.440	14.477	14.514	14.550	14.587	14.624	14.660
6.0	14.697	14.734	14.770	14.807	14.844	14.881	14.918	14.955	14.992	15.029
6.1	15.066	15.103	15.140	15.177	15.214	15.252	15.289	15.326	15.363	15.401
6.2	15.438	15.475	15.513	15.550	15.588	15.625	15.663	15.700	15.738	15.775
6.3	15.813	15.851	15.888	15.926	15.964	16.001	16.039	16.077	16.115	16.153
6.4	16.191	16.229	16.267	16.305	16.343	16.381	16.419	16.457	16.495	16.534
6.5	16.572	16.610	16.648	16.687	16.725	16.763	16.802	16.840	16.879	16.917
6.6	16.956	16.994	17.033	17.071	17.110	17.149	17.187	17.226	17.265	17.304
6.7	17.343	17.381	17.420	17.459	17.498	17.537	17.576	17.615	17.654	17.693
6.8	17.732	17.771	17.811	17.850	17.889	17.928	17.967	18.007	18.046	18.085
6.9	18.125	18.164	18.204	18.243	18.283	18.322	18.362	18.401	18.441	18.481
7.0	18.520	18.560	18.600	18.639	18.679	18.719	18.759	18.799	18.839	18.879
7.1	18.919	18.959	18.999	19.039	19.079	19.119	19.159	19.199	19.239	19.279
7.2	19.320	19.360	19.400	19.441	19.481	19.521	19.562	19.602	19.643	19.683
7.3	19.724	19.764	19.805	19.845	19.886	19.926	19.967	20.008	20.049	20.089
7.4	20.130	20.171	20.212	20.253	20.294	20.335	20.375	20.416	20.457	20.499
7.5	20.540	20.581	20.622	20.663	20.704	20.745	20.787	20.828	20.869	20.910
7.6	20.952	20.993	21.035	21.076	21.117	21.159	21.200	21.242	21.283	21.325
7.7	21.367	21.408	21.450	21.492	21.533	21.575	21.617	21.659	21.700	21.742
7.8	21.784	21.826	21.868	21.910	21.952	21.994	22.036	22.078	22.120	22.162
7.9	22.204	22.247	22.289	22.331	22.373	22.416	22.458	22.500	22.543	22.585
8.0	22.627	22.670	22.712	22.755	22.797	22.840	22.882	22.925	22.968	23.010
8.1	23.053	23.096	23.138	23.181	23.224	23.267	23.310	23.352	23.395	23.438
8.2	23.481	23.524	23.567	23.610	23.653	23.696	23.739	23.783	23.826	23.869
8.3	23.912	23.955	23.999	24.042	24.085	24.128	24.172	24.215	24.259	24.302
8.4	24.346	24.389	24.433	24.476	24.520	24.563	24.607	24.650	24.694	24.738
8.5	24.782	24.825	24.869	24.913	24.957	25.001	25.044	25.088	25.132	25.176
8.6	25.220	25.264	25.308	25.352	25.396	25.440	25.485	25.529	25.573	25.617
8.7	25.661	25.706	25.750	25.794	25.838	25.883	25.927	25.972	26.016	26.061
8.8	26.105	26.150	26.194	26.239	26.283	26.328	26.372	26.417	26.462	26.507
8.9	26.551	26.596	26.641	26.686	26.730	26.775	26.820	26.865	26.910	26.955
9.0	27.000	27.045	27.090	27.135	27.180	27.225	27.270	27.316	27.361	27.406
9.1	27.451	27.497	27.542	27.587	27.632	27.678	27.723	27.769	27.814	27.859
9.2	27.905	27.950	27.996	28.042	28.087	28.133	28.178	28.224	28.270	28.315
9.3	28.361	28.407	28.453	28.499	28.544	28.590	28.636	28.682	28.728	28.774
9.4	28.820	28.866	28.912	28.958	29.004	29.050	29.096	29.142	29.189	29.235
9.5	29.281	29.327	29.373	29.420	29.466	29.512	29.559	29.605	29.652	29.698
9.6	29.745	29.791	29.838	29.884	29.931	29.977	30.024	30.070	30.117	30.164
9.7	30.210	30.257	30.304	30.351	30.398	30.444	30.491	30.538	30.585	30.632
9.8	30.679	30.726	30.773	30.820	30.867	30.914	30.961	31.008	31.055	31.102
9.9	31.150	31.197	31.244	31.291	31.339	31.386	31.433	31.481	31.528	31.575
10.0	31.623	31.670	31.718	31.765	31.813	31.860	31.908	31.955	32.003	32.051

*Useful for hydraulic head computations.

1.6   Five-halves Powers of Numbers*

	0.00	0.01	0.02	0.03	0.04	0.05	0.06	0.07	0.08	0.09
0.0	0.00	0.00	0.00	0.00	0.00	0.00	0.00	0.00	0.00	0.00
0.1	0.00	0.00	0.00	0.01	0.01	0.01	0.01	0.01	0.01	0.02
0.2	0.02	0.02	0.02	0.03	0.03	0.03	0.03	0.04	0.04	0.05
0.3	0.05	0.05	0.06	0.06	0.07	0.07	0.08	0.08	0.09	0.09
0.4	0.10	0.11	0.11	0.12	0.13	0.14	0.14	0.15	0.16	0.17
0.5	0.18	0.19	0.19	0.20	0.21	0.22	0.23	0.25	0.26	0.27
0.6	0.28	0.29	0.30	0.32	0.33	0.34	0.35	0.37	0.38	0.40
0.7	0.41	0.42	0.44	0.46	0.47	0.49	0.50	0.52	0.54	0.55
0.8	0.57	0.59	0.61	0.63	0.65	0.67	0.69	0.71	0.73	0.75
0.9	0.77	0.79	0.81	0.83	0.86	0.88	0.90	0.93	0.95	0.98
1.0	1.00	1.03	1.05	1.08	1.10	1.13	1.16	1.18	1.21	1.24
1.1	1.27	1.30	1.33	1.36	1.39	1.42	1.45	1.48	1.51	1.54
1.2	1.58	1.61	1.64	1.68	1.71	1.75	1.78	1.82	1.85	1.89
1.3	1.93	1.96	2.00	2.04	2.08	2.12	2.16	2.20	2.24	2.28
1.4	2.32	2.36	2.40	2.45	2.49	2.53	2.58	2.62	2.66	2.71
1.5	2.76	2.80	2.85	2.90	2.94	2.99	3.04	3.09	3.14	3.19
1.6	3.24	3.29	3.34	3.39	3.44	3.50	3.55	3.60	3.66	3.71
1.7	3.77	3.82	3.88	3.94	3.99	4.05	4.11	4.17	4.23	4.29
1.8	4.35	4.41	4.47	4.53	4.59	4.66	4.72	4.78	4.85	4.91
1.9	4.98	5.04	5.11	5.17	5.24	5.31	5.38	5.45	5.52	5.59
2.0	5.66	5.73	5.80	5.87	5.94	6.02	6.09	6.16	6.24	6.31
2.1	6.39	6.47	6.54	6.62	6.70	6.78	6.86	6.94	7.02	7.10
2.2	7.18	7.26	7.34	7.43	7.51	7.59	7.68	7.76	7.85	7.94
2.3	8.02	8.11	8.20	8.29	8.38	8.47	8.56	8.65	8.74	8.83
2.4	8.92	9.02	9.11	9.20	9.30	9.40	9.49	9.59	9.69	9.78
2.5	9.88	9.98	10.08	10.18	10.28	10.38	10.49	10.59	10.69	10.80
2.6	10.90	11.01	11.11	11.22	11.32	11.43	11.54	11.65	11.76	11.87
2.7	11.98	12.09	12.20	12.31	12.43	12.54	12.66	12.77	12.89	13.00
2.8	13.12	13.24	13.35	13.47	13.59	13.71	13.83	13.95	14.08	14.20
2.9	14.32	14.45	14.57	14.69	14.82	14.95	15.07	15.20	15.33	15.46
3.0	15.59	15.72	15.85	15.98	16.11	16.25	16.38	16.51	16.65	16.78
3.1	16.92	17.06	17.19	17.33	17.47	17.61	17.75	17.89	18.03	18.18
3.2	18.32	18.46	18.61	18.75	18.90	19.04	19.19	19.34	19.48	19.63
3.3	19.78	19.93	20.08	20.24	20.39	20.54	20.69	20.85	21.00	21.16
3.4	21.32	21.47	21.63	21.79	21.95	22.11	22.27	22.43	22.59	22.75
3.5	22.92	23.08	23.25	23.41	23.58	23.74	23.91	24.08	24.25	24.42
3.6	24.59	24.76	24.93	25.11	25.28	25.45	25.63	25.80	25.98	26.16
3.7	26.33	26.51	26.69	26.87	27.05	27.23	27.41	27.60	27.78	27.96
3.8	28.15	28.33	28.52	28.71	28.90	29.08	29.27	29.46	29.65	29.85
3.9	30.04	30.23	30.42	30.62	30.81	31.01	31.21	31.40	31.60	31.80
4.0	32.00	32.20	32.40	32.60	32.81	33.01	33.21	33.42	33.62	33.83
4.1	34.04	34.25	34.45	34.66	34.87	35.08	35.30	35.51	35.72	35.94
4.2	36.15	36.37	36.58	36.80	37.02	37.24	37.46	37.68	37.90	38.12
4.3	38.34	38.56	38.79	39.01	39.24	39.47	39.69	39.92	40.15	40.38
4.4	40.61	40.84	41.07	41.31	41.54	41.77	42.01	42.24	42.48	42.72
4.5	42.96	43.20	43.44	43.68	43.92	44.16	44.40	44.65	44.89	45.14
4.6	45.38	45.63	45.88	46.13	46.38	46.63	46.88	47.13	47.38	47.64
4.7	47.89	48.15	48.40	48.66	48.92	49.17	49.43	49.69	49.95	50.22
4.8	50.48	50.74	51.01	51.27	51.54	51.80	52.07	52.34	52.61	52.88
4.9	53.15	53.42	53.69	53.97	54.24	54.51	54.79	55.07	55.34	55.62
5.0	55.90	56.18	56.46	56.74	57.03	57.31	57.59	57.88	58.16	58.45

*Useful for hydraulic head computations.

1.6 Five-halves Powers of Numbers (continued)*

	0.00	0.01	0.02	0.03	0.04	0.05	0.06	0.07	0.08	0.09
5.1	58.74	59.03	59.32	59.61	59.90	60.19	60.48	60.78	61.07	61.36
5.2	61.66	61.96	62.26	62.55	62.85	63.15	63.45	63.76	64.06	64.36
5.3	64.67	64.97	65.28	65.59	65.90	66.20	66.51	66.82	67.14	67.45
5.4	67.76	68.08	68.39	68.71	69.02	69.34	69.66	69.98	70.30	70.62
5.5	70.94	71.27	71.59	71.91	72.24	72.57	72.89	73.22	73.55	73.88
5.6	74.21	74.54	74.88	75.21	75.54	75.88	76.22	76.55	76.89	77.23
5.7	77.57	77.91	78.25	78.59	78.94	79.28	79.63	79.97	80.32	80.67
5.8	81.02	81.37	81.72	82.07	82.42	82.77	83.13	83.48	83.84	84.20
5.9	84.55	84.91	85.27	85.63	85.99	86.36	86.72	87.08	87.45	87.81
6.0	88.18	88.55	88.92	89.29	89.66	90.03	90.40	90.78	91.15	91.53
6.1	91.90	92.28	92.66	93.04	93.42	93.80	94.18	94.56	94.94	95.33
6.2	95.71	96.10	96.49	96.88	97.27	97.66	98.05	98.44	98.83	99.23
6.3	99.62	100.0	100.4	100.8	101.2	101.6	102.0	102.4	102.8	103.2
6.4	103.6	104.0	104.4	104.8	105.2	105.7	106.1	106.5	106.9	107.3
6.5	107.7	108.1	108.5	109.0	109.4	109.8	110.2	110.6	111.1	111.5
6.6	111.9	112.3	112.8	113.2	113.6	114.0	114.5	114.9	115.3	115.8
6.7	116.2	116.6	117.1	117.5	117.9	118.4	118.8	119.3	119.7	120.1
6.8	120.6	121.0	121.5	121.9	122.4	122.8	123.3	123.7	124.2	124.6
6.9	125.1	125.5	126.0	126.4	126.9	127.3	127.8	128.3	128.7	129.2
7.0	129.6	130.1	130.6	131.0	131.5	132.0	132.4	132.9	133.4	133.8
7.1	134.3	134.8	135.3	135.7	136.2	136.7	137.2	137.7	138.1	138.6
7.2	139.1	139.6	140.1	140.6	141.0	141.5	142.0	142.5	143.0	143.5
7.3	144.0	144.5	145.0	145.5	146.0	146.5	147.0	147.5	148.0	148.5
7.4	149.0	149.5	150.0	150.5	151.0	151.5	152.0	152.5	153.0	153.5
7.5	154.0	154.6	155.1	155.6	156.1	156.6	157.1	157.7	158.2	158.7
7.6	159.2	159.8	160.3	160.8	161.3	161.9	162.4	162.9	163.5	164.0
7.7	164.5	165.1	165.6	166.1	166.7	167.2	167.7	168.3	168.8	169.4
7.8	169.9	170.5	171.0	171.6	172.1	172.7	173.2	173.8	174.3	174.9
7.9	175.4	176.0	176.5	177.1	177.6	178.2	178.8	179.3	179.9	180.5
8.0	181.0	181.6	182.2	182.7	183.3	183.9	184.4	185.0	185.6	186.2
8.1	186.7	187.3	187.9	188.5	189.0	189.6	190.2	190.8	191.4	192.0
8.2	192.5	193.1	193.7	194.3	194.9	195.5	196.1	196.7	197.3	197.9
8.3	198.5	199.1	199.7	200.3	200.9	201.5	202.1	202.7	203.3	203.9
8.4	204.5	205.1	205.7	206.3	206.9	207.6	208.2	208.8	209.4	210.0
8.5	210.6	211.3	211.9	212.5	213.1	213.8	214.4	215.0	215.6	216.3
8.6	216.9	217.5	218.2	218.8	219.4	220.1	220.7	221.3	222.0	222.6
8.7	223.3	223.9	224.5	225.2	225.8	226.5	227.1	227.8	228.4	229.1
8.8	229.7	230.4	231.0	231.7	232.3	233.0	233.7	234.3	235.0	235.6
8.9	236.3	237.0	237.6	238.3	239.0	239.6	240.3	241.0	241.7	242.3
9.0	243.0	243.7	244.4	245.0	245.7	246.4	247.1	247.8	248.4	249.1
9.1	249.8	250.5	251.2	251.9	252.6	253.3	253.9	254.6	255.3	256.0
9.2	256.7	257.4	258.1	258.8	259.5	260.2	260.9	261.6	262.3	263.1
9.3	263.8	264.5	265.2	265.9	266.6	267.3	268.0	268.8	269.5	270.2
9.4	270.9	271.6	272.3	273.1	273.8	274.5	275.3	276.0	276.7	277.4
9.5	278.2	278.9	279.6	280.4	281.1	281.8	282.6	283.3	284.1	284.8
9.6	285.5	286.3	287.0	287.8	288.5	289.3	290.0	290.8	291.5	292.3
9.7	293.0	293.8	294.6	295.3	296.1	296.8	297.6	298.4	299.1	299.9
9.8	300.7	301.4	302.2	303.0	303.7	304.5	305.3	306.1	306.8	307.6
9.9	308.4	309.2	309.9	310.7	311.5	312.3	313.1	313.9	314.6	315.4
10.0	316.2	317.0	317.8	318.6	319.4	320.2	321.0	321.8	322.6	323.4

*Useful for hydraulic head computations.

2

Trigonometric Relationships and Tables

2.1   Oblique Angled Triangles—Solutions (see Figure 1)

Known	α	β	θ	b	c
			Required		
a, b, c	$\tan \tfrac{1}{2}\alpha =$ $K/(s-a)$	$\tan \tfrac{1}{2}\beta =$ $K/(s-b)$	$\tan \tfrac{1}{2}\theta =$ $K/(s-c)$		
a, α, β			$180° - (\alpha + \beta)$	$a \sin \beta/$ $\sin \alpha$	$a \sin \theta/$ $\sin \alpha$
a, b, α		$\sin \beta =$ $b/a \sin \alpha$	$180° - (\alpha + \beta)$		$b \sin \theta/$ $\sin \beta$
a, b, θ	$\tan \alpha =$ $a \sin \theta/(b - a \cos \theta)$				$\sqrt{a^2 + b^2 - 2ab \cos \theta}$

Oblique Angled Triangles—Definitions

$$a^2 = b^2 + c^2 - 2bc \cos \alpha$$
$$b^2 = a^2 + c^2 - 2ac \cos \beta$$
$$c^2 = a^2 + b^2 - 2ab \cos \theta$$

$$s = (a + b + c)/2$$
$$K = \sqrt{(s-a)(s-b)(s-c)/s}$$
$$Area = \tfrac{1}{2} ab \sin \theta$$

2.2   Right Angled Triangles (see Figure 2)

Known	α	β	a	b	c
			Required		
a, b	$\tan \alpha = a/b$	$\tan \beta = b/a$			$\sqrt{(a^2 + b^2)}$
a, c	$\sin \alpha = a/c$	$\cos \beta = a/c$		$\sqrt{(c^2 - a^2)}$	
α, a		$90° - \alpha$		$a \cot \alpha$	$a/\sin \alpha$
α, b		$90° - \alpha$	$b \tan \alpha$		$b/\cos \alpha$
α, c		$90° - \alpha$	$c \sin \alpha$	$c \cos \alpha$	

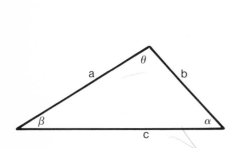

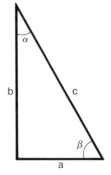

Figure 1   Oblique Angled Triangles   Figure 2   Right Angled Triangles

2.3   General Trigonometric Relationships (see Figure 2) _____

Functions of Acute Angles

$\sin \alpha = a/c$
$\cos \alpha = b/c$
$\tan \alpha = a/b$
$\cot \alpha = b/a$
$\sec \alpha = c/b$
$\csc \alpha = c/a$

Pythagorean Relations

$c^2 = a^2 + b^2$
$\sin^2 \alpha + \cos^2 \alpha = 1$
$\sec^2 \alpha - \tan^2 \alpha = 1$
$\csc^2 \alpha - \cot^2 \alpha = 1$

2.4   Relative Accuracy of Computed Lengths and Angles _____

The following should be observed when solving a triangle for any of its parts:

Significant figures for sides	Requires angle to nearest
2 significant digits	degree
3 significant digits	10 minutes
4 significant digits	minute
5 significant digits	0.1 minute

2.5   Minutes to Decimals of a Degree

Minutes	Degrees	Minutes	Degrees	Minutes	Degrees
1	0.02	21	0.35	41	0.68
2	0.03	22	0.37	42	0.70
3	0.05	23	0.38	43	0.72
4	0.07	24	0.40	44	0.73
5	0.08	25	0.42	45	0.75
6	0.10	26	0.43	46	0.77
7	0.12	27	0.45	47	0.78
8	0.13	28	0.47	48	0.80
9	0.15	29	0.48	49	0.82
10	0.17	30	0.50	50	0.83
11	0.18	31	0.52	51	0.85
12	0.20	32	0.53	52	0.87
13	0.22	33	0.55	53	0.88
14	0.23	34	0.57	54	0.90
15	0.25	35	0.58	55	0.92
16	0.27	36	0.60	56	0.93
17	0.28	37	0.62	57	0.95
18	0.30	38	0.63	58	0.97
19	0.32	39	0.65	59	0.98
20	0.33	40	0.67	60	1.00

2.6   Decimals of a Degree to Minutes and Seconds

Degrees	Minutes	Seconds	Degrees	Minutes	Seconds
0.01	0	36	0.51	30	36
0.02	1	12	0.52	31	12
0.03	1	48	0.53	31	48
0.04	2	24	0.54	32	24
0.05	3	0	0.55	33	0
0.06	3	36	0.56	33	36
0.07	4	12	0.57	34	12
0.08	4	48	0.58	34	48
0.09	5	24	0.59	35	24
0.10	6	0	0.60	36	0
0.11	6	36	0.61	36	36
0.12	7	12	0.62	37	12
0.13	7	48	0.63	37	48
0.14	8	24	0.64	38	24
0.15	9	0	0.65	39	0
0.16	9	36	0.66	39	36
0.17	10	12	0.67	40	12
0.18	10	48	0.68	40	48
0.19	11	24	0.69	41	24
0.20	12	0	0.70	42	0
0.21	12	36	0.71	42	36
0.22	13	12	0.72	43	12
0.23	13	48	0.73	43	48
0.24	14	24	0.74	44	24
0.25	15	0	0.75	45	0
0.26	15	36	0.76	45	36
0.27	16	12	0.77	46	12
0.28	16	48	0.78	46	48
0.29	17	24	0.79	47	24
0.30	18	0	0.80	48	0
0.31	18	36	0.81	48	36
0.32	19	12	0.82	49	12
0.33	19	48	0.83	49	48
0.34	20	24	0.84	50	24
0.35	21	0	0.85	51	0
0.36	21	36	0.86	51	36
0.37	22	12	0.87	52	12
0.38	22	48	0.88	52	48
0.39	23	24	0.89	53	24
0.40	24	0	0.90	54	0
0.41	24	36	0.91	54	36
0.42	25	12	0.92	55	12
0.43	25	48	0.93	55	48
0.44	26	24	0.94	56	24
0.45	27	0	0.95	57	0
0.46	27	36	0.96	57	36
0.47	28	12	0.97	58	12
0.48	28	48	0.98	58	48
0.49	29	24	0.99	59	24
0.50	30	0	1.00	60	0

3

Statistical Formulas and Tables

3.1   Definitions and Formulas

Mean: $\overline{X} = (\Sigma X)/n$

Standard deviation: $s = \sqrt{\Sigma (X - \overline{X})^2 / (n - 1)}$

Median: The value of the middle variate in an ordered array of variates or, if n is even, the value of the midpoint between the middle pair of variates.

Mode: In an array of variates, the value represented by the greatest number of the same individual values. When seen in a frequency distribution, it is the value at which the frequency curve peaks.

Variance: s^2

Coefficient of variation: $CV = s/\overline{X}$

Sample size equation: $n = t^2 s^2 / E^2$

> Where: t = student's t at the desired probability level
> s^2 = an estimate of the population variance
> E = the specified sampling error.

Plotting position formulas for event frequency analysis:

> General formula: $P = \dfrac{m-a}{N-a-b + 1}$

> Where: m = the ordered sequence of items in descending order, largest equal to 1
> N = the number of items in data set
> a and b = empirically-derived distribution parameters.

Based on Chow (1964), the following values of a and b are available from the literature:

Source	a	b
Chegodayev	0.3	0.3
Tukey	0.33	0.34
Gringorten	0.44	0.44

Hazen formula: $P = \dfrac{m - 0.5}{N}$

Weibull formula: $P = \dfrac{m}{N + 1}$

3.2 Design Event Recurrence Intervals (Years) Associated With a Given Design Life and Chance of Failure

Design Life Years	Percent Chance of Failure										
	0.5	1	2	5	10	15	20	25	30	40	50
1	200	100	50	20	10	7	5	4	3	3	2
2	399	199	99	39	19	13	9	7	6	4	3
3	599	299	149	59	29	19	14	11	9	6	5
4	798	398	198	78	38	25	18	14	12	8	6
5	998	498	248	98	48	31	23	18	15	10	8
10	1995	995	495	195	95	62	45	35	29	20	15
15	2993	1493	743	293	143	93	68	53	43	30	22
20	3990	1990	990	390	190	124	90	70	57	40	29
25	4988	2488	1238	488	238	154	113	87	71	49	37
30	5985	2985	1485	585	285	185	135	105	85	59	44
35	6983	3483	1733	683	333	216	157	122	99	69	51
40	7980	3980	1980	780	380	247	180	140	113	79	58
45	8978	4478	2228	878	428	277	202	157	127	89	65
50	9975	4975	2475	975	475	308	225	174	141	98	73
60	11 970	5970	2970	1170	570	370	269	209	169	118	87
70	13 965	6965	3465	1365	665	431	314	244	197	138	101
80	15 960	7960	3960	1560	760	493	359	279	225	157	116
90	17 955	8955	4455	1755	855	554	404	313	253	177	130
100	19 950	9950	4950	1950	950	616	449	348	281	196	145

3.3 Suggested Confidence Levels for Hydrologic Data

Percent Confidence	Use of the Data
>>99	Human life at stake
≥99	General health and safety issues; litigation
≥95	Published research; sensitive resource issues
≥85	Moderately sensitive resource issues
≥75	Administrative studies; nonsensitive resource issues

4

Conversion Factors

4.1   Conversion Factors*

To convert		Multiply by		To obtain
Acceleration				
feet per second per second	ft/s²	0.304 800	m/s²	metres per second per second
feet per second per second	ft/s²	30.480 000	cm/s²	centimetres per second per second
metres per second per second	m/s²	3.280 840	ft/s²	feet per second per second
centimetres per second per second	cm/s²	0.032 808	ft/s²	feet per second per second
Area				
acres	acre	0.404 687	ha	hectares
acres	acre	43 560	ft²	square feet
acres	acre	0.004 047	km²	square kilometres
acres	acre	4046.8726	m²	square metres
acres	acre	0.001 563	mi²	square miles
acres	acre	4840	yd²	square yards
hectares	ha	2.471 044	acre	acres
square centimetres	cm²	0.001 076	ft²	square feet
square centimetres	cm²	0.155 000	in.²	square inches
square feet	ft²	0.000 022 96	acre	acres
square feet	ft²	929.0304	cm²	square centimetres
square feet	ft²	144	in.²	square inches
square feet	ft²	0.092 903	m²	square metres
square feet	ft²	3.5870×10^{-8}	mi²	square miles
square feet	ft²	0.111 111	yd²	square yards
square inches	in.²	6.451 600	cm²	square centimetres
square inches	in.²	0.006 944	ft²	square feet
square inches	in.²	645.160	mm²	square millimetres
square kilometres	km²	247.104 393	acre	acres
square kilometres	km²	0.386 101	mi²	square miles
square metres	m²	0.000 247	acre	acres
square metres	m²	10.763 910	ft²	square feet
square metres	m²	1.195 990	yd²	square yards
square miles	mi²	27 878 400	ft²	square feet
square miles	mi²	640	acre	acres
square miles	mi²	2.589 998	km²	square kilometres
square millimetres	mm²	0.001 550	in.²	square inches
square yards	yd²	0.000 207	acre	acres
square yards	yd²	9	ft²	square feet
square yards	yd²	0.836 127	m²	square metres
township	township	36	mi²	square miles
Heat				
British thermal units	btu	251.996	g-cal	gram calories
British thermal units [International Table]	btu	1055.056	J	joules
British thermal units per hour	btu/h	0.070	g-cal/s	gram calories per second
gram calories	g-cal	0.003 968	btu	British thermal units
gram calories	g-cal	0.238 846	J	joules
gram calories per second	g-cal/s	14.285 941	btu/h	British thermal units per hour
joules	J	0.000 948	btu	British thermal units
joules	J	4.186 797	g-cal	gram calories

*The conversion factors in this table are based on information given in *Factors for High-Precision Conversion* (National Bureau of Standards, 1976), *Standard for Metric Practice* (American Society for Testing and Materials, 1980), and *Smithsonian Meteorological Tables* (List, 1968). For units of length, the basic conversion factor of 1 in. = 2.54 cm is used throughout this book. For units of area involving land survey, the basic conversion factor of 1 ft = 1200/3937 m (1 in. = 2.540 005 1 cm) is used. Guidelines for rounding converted units are discussed in the introduction to this book.

4.1   Conversion Factors (continued)

To convert		Multiply by		To obtain
Temperature				
degrees Celsius	°C	9/5 (°C) + 32	°F	degrees Fahrenheit
degrees Celsius	°C	°C + 273.15	K	degrees Kelvin
degrees Fahrenheit	°F	5/9 (°F−32)	°C	degrees Celsius
degrees Fahrenheit	°F	5/9 (°F-32) + 273.15	K	degrees Kelvin
degrees Kelvin	K	K-273.15	°C	degrees Celsius
degrees Kelvin	K	1.80 (K-273.15) + 32	°F	degrees Fahrenheit
Length				
centimetres	cm	0.032 808	ft	feet
centimetres	cm	0.393 701	in.	inches
feet	ft	30.480 000	cm	centimetres
feet	ft	0.000 305	km	kilometres
feet	ft	0.304 800	m	metres
inches	in.	2.540 000	cm	centimetres
inches	in.	25.400 000	mm	millimetres
kilometres	km	3280.839 895	ft	feet
kilometres	km	0.621 371	mi	miles
metres	m	3.280 840	ft	feet
metres	m	1 000 000	μm	micrometres (microns)
metres	m	1.093 613	yd	yards
micrometres (microns)	μm	0.000 001	m	metres
miles [stat]	mi	5280	ft	feet
miles [stat]	mi	1.609 344	km	kilometres
miles [naut]	mi	1.151 555	mi	miles [stat]
miles [stat]	mi	0.868 391	mi	miles [naut]
millimetres	mm	0.039 370	in.	inches
yards	yd	0.914 400	m	metres
Mass				
grains	gr	0.064 799	g	grams
grains	gr	0.002 286	oz	ounces [avdp]
grams	g	15.432 358	gr	grains
grams	g	0.035 274	oz	ounces [avdp]
grams	g	0.002 205	lb	pounds
kilograms	kg	2.204 623	lb	pounds
kilograms	kg	35.273 962	oz	ounces [avdp]
kilograms	kg	0.001 102	ton	tons
kilograms	kg	0.001	tonne	tonnes
milligrams	mg	2.2046×10^{-6}	lb	pounds
milligrams	mg	1.1026×10^{-9}	ton	tons
ounces [avdp]	oz	437.5	gr	grains
ounces [avdp]	oz	28.349 523	g	grams
ounces [avdp]	oz	0.028 350	kg	kilograms
ounces [avdp]	oz	0.911 458	oz	ounces [troy]
ounces [troy]	oz	1.097 143	oz	ounces [avdp]
ounces [avdp]	oz	0.0625	lb	pounds
pounds	lb	453.592 37	g	grams
pounds	lb	0.453 592	kg	kilograms
pounds	lb	453 592.37	mg	milligrams
pounds	lb	16	oz	ounces [avdp]
pounds	lb	0.0005	ton	tons
tons	ton	907.184 74	kg	kilograms
tons	ton	907 184 740	mg	milligrams
tons	ton	2000	lb	pounds
tons	ton	0.892 857	ton	tons [long]
tons [long]	ton	1.12	ton	tons
tons	ton	0.907 185	tonne	tonnes
tonnes	tonne	1000	kg	kilogram
tonnes	tonne	1.102 311	ton	tons

4.1   Conversion Factors (continued)

To convert		Multiply by		To obtain
Mass/Area				
kilograms per hectare	kg/ha	0.892 183	lb/acre	pounds per acre
kilograms per hectare	kg/ha	0.1	tonne/km^2	tonnes per square kilometre
pounds per acre	lb/acre	1.120 847	kg/ha	kilograms per hectare
pounds per acre	lb/acre	0.001 121	tonne/ha	tonnes per hectare
pounds per acre	lb/acre	0.320 000	ton/mi^2	tons per square mile
tonnes per hectare	tonne/ha	892.1827	lb/acre	pounds per acre
tonnes per hectare	tonne/ha	0.446 091	ton/acre	tons per acre
tonnes per square kilometre	tonne/km^2	10	kg/ha	kilograms per hectare
tonnes per square kilometre	tonne/km^2	2.854 985	ton/mi^2	tons per square mile
tons per acre	ton/acre	2.241 693	tonne/ha	tonnes per hectare
tons per acre	ton/acre	640	ton/mi^2	tons per square mile
tons per square mile	ton/mi^2	0.350 265	tonne/km^2	tonnes per square kilometre
tons per square mile	ton/mi^2	0.001 563	ton/acre	tons per acre
Mass/Volume or Density				
grams per cubic centimetre	g/cm^3	1000	kg/m^3	kilograms per cubic metre
grams per cubic centimetre	g/cm^3	62.427 961	lb/ft^3	pounds per cubic foot
grams per cubic centimetre	g/cm^3	1	tonne/m^3	tonnes per cubic metre
grams per cubic centimetre	g/cm^3	1359.680 98	ton/acre-ft	tons per acre-foot
kilograms per cubic metre	kg/m^3	0.001	g/cm^3	grams per cubic centimetre
kilograms per cubic metre	kg/m^3	0.062 428	lb/ft^3	pounds per cubic foot
kilograms per cubic metre	kg/m^3	1.359 681	ton/acre-ft	tons per acre-foot
pounds per cubic foot	lb/ft^3	0.016 018	g/cm^3	grams per cubic centimetre
pounds per cubic foot	lb/ft^3	16.018 463	kg/m^3	kilograms per cubic metre
pounds per cubic foot	lb/ft^3	0.016 018	tonnne/m^3	tonnes per cubic metre
pounds per cubic foot	lb/ft^3	0.013 500	ton/yd^3	tons per cubic yard
tonnes per cubic metre	tonne/m^3	1	g/cm^3	grams per cubic centimetre
tonnes per cubic metre	tonne/m^3	62.427 961	lb/ft^3	pounds per cubic foot
tonnes per cubic metre	tonne/m^3	0.842 777	ton/yd^3	tons per cubic yard
tons per acre-foot	ton/acre-ft	0.000 735	g/cm^3	grams per cubic centimetre
tons per acre-foot	ton/acre-ft	0.735 467	kg/m^3	kilograms per cubic metre
tons per cubic yard	ton/yd^3	74.074 074	lb/ft^3	pounds per cubic foot
tons per cubic yard	ton/yd^3	1.186 553	tonne/m^3	tonnes per cubic metre
Pressure				
feet of water @ 50°F	ft H$_2$O	304.708 86	kg/m^2	kilograms per square metre
feet of water @ 50°F	ft H$_2$O	62.409 29	lb/ft^2	pounds per square foot
kilograms per square centimetre	kg/cm^2	10 000	kg/m^2	kilograms per square metre
kilograms per square centimetre	kg/cm^2	14.223 34	lb/in.^{2}	pounds per square inch
kilograms per square metre	kg/m^2	0.003 28	ft H$_2$O	feet of water @ 50°F
kilograms per square metre	kg/m^2	0.0001	kg/cm^2	kilograms per square centimetre
kilograms per square metre	kg/m^2	0.204 82	lb/ft^2	pounds per square foot
pounds per square foot	lb/ft^2	0.016 02	ft H$_2$O	feet of water @ 50°F
pounds per square foot	lb/ft^2	4.882 43	kg/m^2	kilograms per square metre
pounds per square foot	lb/ft^2	0.006 94	lb/in.^{2}	pounds per square inch
pounds per square inch	lb/in.^{2}	0.070 31	kg/cm^2	kilograms per square centimetre
pounds per square inch	lb/in.^{2}	144	lb/ft^2	pounds per square foot
Time				
days	d	1440	min	minutes
days	d	86 400	s	seconds
hours	h	3600	s	seconds
minutes	min	0.000 694 4	d	days
seconds	s	1.157×10^{-5}	d	days
seconds	s	2.778×10^{-5}	h	hours
Velocity				
feet per second	ft/s	0.304 800	m/s	metres per second
feet per second	ft/s	0.681 818	mph	miles per hour
kilometres per hour	km/h	0.277 778	m/s	metres per second
kilometres per hour	km/h	0.621 371	mph	miles per hour

4.1   Conversion Factors (continued)

To convert		Multiply by		To obtain
knots	kn	1.151 555	mph	miles per hour
metres per second	m/s	3.280 840	ft/s	feet per second
metres per second	m/s	3.6	km/h	kilometres per hour
miles per hour	mph	1.466 667	ft/s	feet per second
miles per hour	mph	1.609 344	km/h	kilometres per hour
miles per hour	mph	0.868 391	kn	knots

Viscosity

To convert		Multiply by		To obtain
centipoise	cP	0.01	P	poise
centipoise	cP	2.089×10^{-5}	lb-s/ft^2	pound-seconds per square foot
centipoise	cP	0.001	Pa.s	pascal second
poise	P	1	g/cm.s	grams per centimetre-second
poise	P	0.002 089	lb-s/ft^2	pound-seconds per square foot
poise	P	0.1	Pa.s	pascal second
pound-seconds per square foot	lb-s/ft^2	47 880	cP	centipoise
pound-seconds per square foot	lb-s/ft^2	478.8	g/cm.s	grams per centimetre seconds
pound-seconds per square foot	lb-s/ft^2	47.88	Pa.s	pascal seconds

Volume and Capacity

To convert		Multiply by		To obtain
acre-feet	acre-ft	43 560	ft^3	cubic feet
acre-feet	acre-ft	0.123 349	ha-m	hectare-metres
acre-feet	acre-ft	1233.489	m^3	cubic metres
cubic centimetres	cm^3	0.061 024	in.^{3}	cubic inches
cubic feet	ft^3	2.2957×10^{-5}	acre-ft	acre-feet
cubic feet	ft^3	0.028 317	m^3	cubic metres
cubic feet	ft^3	0.037 037	yd^3	cubic yards
hectare-metres	ha-m	8.107 100	acre-ft	acre-feet
cubic inches	in.^{3}	16.387 064	cm^3	cubic centimetres
cubic kilometres	km^3	0.239 913	mi^3	cubic miles
cubic metres	m^3	8.1071×10^{-4}	acre-ft	acre-feet
cubic metres	m^3	35.314 667	ft^3	cubic feet
cubic metres	m^3	1.307 951	yd^3	cubic yards
cubic miles	mi^3	4.168 182	km^3	cubic kilometres
cubic yards	yd^3	27	ft^3	cubic feet
cubic yards	yd^3	0.764 555	m^3	cubic metres
barrels [beer, 31-gal]	bbl	4.144 10	ft^3	cubic feet
barrels [wine, 31.5-gal]	bbl	4.210 94	ft^3	cubic feet
barrels [oil, 42-gal]	bbl	5.614 58	ft^3	cubic feet
barrels [whiskey, 45-gal]	bbl	6.015 63	ft^3	cubic feet
barrels [55-gal]	bbl	7.352 43	ft^3	cubic feet
cubic centimetres	cm^3	0.999 97	mL	millilitres
cubic feet	ft^3	0.241 31	bbl	barrel [beer, 31-gal]
cubic feet	ft^3	0.237 48	bbl	barrel [wine, 31.5-gal]
cubic feet	ft^3	0.178 11	bbl	barrel [oil, 42-gal]
cubic feet	ft^3	0.166 23	bbl	barrel [whiskey, 45-gal]
cubic feet	ft^3	0.136 01	bbl	barrel [55-gal]
cubic feet	ft^3	7.480 52	gal	gallons
cubic feet	ft^3	28.316 84	L	litres
cubic inches	in.^{3}	0.016 39	L	litres
gallons	gal	0.133 68	ft^3	cubic feet
gallons	gal	0.832 67	Imp gal	Imperial gallons
gallons	gal	3.785 41	L	litres
litres	L	0.035 31	ft^3	cubic feet
litres	L	61.023 76	in.^{3}	cubic inches
litres	L	0.264 17	gal	gallons
litres	L	1.056 69	qt	quarts
millilitres	mL	1.000 00	cm^3	cubic centimetres
millilitres	mL	0.033 81	oz	ounces
ounces	oz	29.573 52	mL	millilitres
quarts	qt	0.946 35	L	litres

4.1   Conversion Factors (continued)

To convert		Multiply by		To obtain
— **Volume/Time or Flow Rate** —				
acre-feet per day	acre-ft/d	0.504 167	ft³/s	cubic feet per second
acre-feet per day	acre-ft/d	0.123 349	ha-m/d	hectare-metres per day
acre-feet per day	acre-ft/d	0.325 851	mgd	million gallons per day
acre-feet per month [28-day]	acre-ft/mo	0.018 006	cfs	cubic feet per second
acre-feet per month [29-day]	acre-ft/mo	0.017 385	cfs	cubic feet per second
acre-feet per month [30-day]	acre-ft/mo	0.016 806	cfs	cubic feet per second
acre-feet per month [31-day]	acre-ft/mo	0.016 263	cfs	cubic feet per second
acre-feet per year	acre-ft/yr	0.001 370	acre-in./h	acre-inches per hour
acre-inches per hour	acre-in./h	2	acre-ft/d	acre-feet per day
acre-inches per hour	acre-in./h	1.008 333	cfs	cubic feet per second
acre-inches per hour	acre-in./h	1.027 906	ha-cm/h	hectare-centimetres per hour
cubic feet per second	cfs	1.983 47	acre-ft/d	acre-feet per day
cubic feet per second	cfs	55.537 19	acre-ft/mo	acre-feet per month [28-day]
cubic feet per second	cfs	57.520 66	acre-ft/mo	acre-feet per month [29-day]
cubic feet per second	cfs	59.504 13	acre-ft/mo	acre-feet per month [30-day]
cubic feet per second	cfs	61.487 60	acre-ft/mo	acre-feet per month [31-day]
cubic feet per second	cfs	723.966 94	acre-ft/yr	acre-feet per year [365 day]
cubic feet per second	cfs	725.950 41	acre-ft/yr	acre-feet per year [366 day]
cubic feet per second	cfs	0.991 74	acre-in./h	acre-inches per hour
cubic feet per second	cfs	60.456 20/acres	cm/d	centimetres per day
cubic feet per second	cfs	2.519 01/acres	cm/h	centimetres per hour
cubic feet per second	cfs	1.699 01	m³/min	cubic metres per minute
cubic feet per second	cfs	0.028 32	m³/s	cubic metres per second
cubic feet per second	cfs	0.000 214 24	mi³/yr	cubic miles per year
cubic feet per second	cfs	6.666 67	yd³/min	cubic yards per minute
cubic feet per second	cfs	448.831 17	gpm	gallons per minute
cubic feet per second	cfs	538 168.7	Imp gpd	Imperial gallons per day
cubic feet per second	cfs	373.73	Imp gpm	Imperial gallons per minute
cubic feet per second	cfs	23.801 65/acres	in./d	inches per day
cubic feet per second	cfs	0.991 74/acres	in./h	inches per hour
cubic feet per second	cfs	28.316 85	L/s	litres per second
cubic feet per second	cfs	0.646 32	mgd	million gals per day
cubic feet per second	cfs	50	miner's in.	miner's inches [Idaho, Kan., S.D., N.D, N.M., Utah, Wash., S.Calif.]
cubic feet per second	cfs	40	miner's in.	miner's inches [Ariz., Mont., Ore., Nev., N. Calif.]
cubic feet per second	cfs	38	miner's in.	miner's inches [Colo.]
cubic feet per second	cfs	2696.082	ton H₂O/d	tons of water [50°F] per day
cubic metres per second	m³/s	864/ha	cm/d	centimetres per day
cubic metres per second	m³/s	315 360/ha	cm/yr	centimetres per year
cubic metres per second	m³/s	35.314 67	cfs	cubic feet per second
cubic metres per second	m³/s	8.640	ha-m/d	hectare-metres per day
cubic metres per second	m³/s	3153.60	ha-m/yr	hectare-metres per year [365 day]
cubic metres per second	m³/s	3162.24	ha-m/yr	hectare-metres per year [366 day]
cubic metres per second	m³/s	86 400 010	L/d	litres per day
cubic metres per second	m³/s	60 000	L/min	litres per minute
cubic metres per second	m³/s	1000.000 12	L/s	litres per second
centimetres per day	cm/d	0.016 54 × acres	cfs	cubic feet per second
centimetres per day	cm/d	0.001 16 × ha	m³/s	cubic metres per second
centimetres per hour	cm/h	0.396 98 × acres	cfs	cubic feet per second
centimetres per year	cm/yr	(3.171×10⁻⁶)×ha	m³/s	cubic metres per second
gallons per day	gpd	0.001 12	acre-ft/yr	acre-feet per year
gallons per minute	gpm	0.004 42	acre-ft/d	acre-feet per day
gallons per minute	gpm	1.613 01	acre-ft/yr	acre-feet per year
gallons per minute	gpm	0.002 23	cfs	cubic feet per second
gallons per minute	gpm	6.309 × 10⁻⁵	m³/s	cubic metres per second
gallons per minute	gpm	0.063 09	L/s	litres per second
Imperial gallons per minute	Imp gpm	0.002 68	cfs	cubic feet per second
million gallons per day	mgd	3.068 88	acre-ft/d	acre-feet per day
million gallons per day	mgd	1.547 23	cfs	cubic feet per second
hectare-metres per day	ha-m/d	8.107 10	acre-ft/d	acre-feet per day
hectare-metres per day	ha-m/d	0.115 74	m³/s	cubic metres per second
hectare-metres per day	ha-m/d	115.740 75	L/s	litres per second

4.1 Conversion Factors (continued)

To convert		Multiply by		To obtain
hectare-metres per year	ha-m/yr	8.107 10	acre-ft/yr	acre-feet per year
hectare-metres per year	ha-m/yr	3.171×10^{-4}	m³/s	cubic metres per second
hectare-metres per year	ha-m/yr	0.317 10	L/s	litres per second
inches per day	in./d	0.042 01 × acres	cfs	cubic feet per second
inches per hour	in./h	1.008 33 × acres	cfs	cubic feet per second
inches per year	in./yr	0.000 115 × acres	cfs	cubic feet per second
litres per second	L/s	0.864/ha	cm/d	centimetres per day
litres per second	L/s	0.036/ha	cm/h	centimetres per hour
litres per second	L/s	315.36/ha	cm/yr	centimetres per year
litres per second	L/s	0.035 31	cfs	cubic feet per second
litres per second	L/s	0.001	m³/s	cubic metres per second
litres per second	L/s	15.850 32	gpm	gallons per minute
miner's inches [Idaho, Kan., Neb., S.D., N.D., N.M., Utah, Wash., S. Calif.]	miner's in.	0.020	cfs	cubic feet per second
miner's inches [Ariz., Mont., Ore., Nev., N. Calif.]	miner's in.	0.025	cfs	cubic feet per second
miner's inches [Colo.]	miner's in.	0.026	cfs	cubic feet per second
acre feet	acre-ft	504.17	Kcfs-d	thousand cfs-days
acre-feet per square mile	acre-ft/mi²	0.047 63	cm	centimetres
acre-feet per square mile	acre-ft/mi²	0.047 63	ha-m/km²	hectare-metres per square kilometre
acre-feet per square mile	acre-ft/mi²	0.018 75	in.	inches
centimetres	cm	20.997 38	acre-ft/mi²	acre-feet per square mile
cfs per square mile	cfs/mi²	0.010 93	(m³/s)/km²	cubic metres per second per square kilometre
cfs per square mile	cfs/mi²	1.041 32	in./mo	inches per month [28 day]
cfs per square mile	cfs/mi²	1.078 51	in./mo	inches per month [29 day]
cfs per square mile	cfs/mi²	1.115 70	in./mo	inches per month [30 day]
cfs per square mile	cfs/mi²	1.152 89	in./mo	inches per month [31 day]
cfs per square mile	cfs/mi²	13.574 38	in./yr	inches per year [365 day]
cfs per square mile	cfs/mi²	13.611 57	in./yr	inches per year [366 day]
cfs per square mile	cfs/mi²	0.037 19	in./d	inches per day
cfs per square mile	cfs/mi²	10.933 20	(L/s)/km²	litres per second per square kilometre
cubic metres per second per square kilometre	(m³/s)/km²	91.464 57	cfs/mi²	cfs per square mile
hectare-metres per square kilometre	ha-m/km²	20.997 29	acre-ft/mi²	acre-feet per square mile
inches	in.	53.333 33	acre-ft/mi²	acre-feet per square mile
inches	in.	0.026 89	Kcfs-d/mi²	thousand cfs-days per square mile
thousand cfs-days per square mile	Kcfs-d/mi²	37.190 08	in.	inches
thousand cfs-days	Kcfs-d	0.001 98	acre-ft	acre-feet
litres per second per square kilometre	(L/s)/km²	0.091 46	cfs/mi²	cfs per square mile
──────── Concentration ────────				
milligrams per litre*	mg/L	1000.30	ppb	parts per billion
milligrams per litre*	mg/L	1.000 30	ppm	parts per million
milligrams per litre	mg/L	0.002 45 × cfs	tonne/d	tonnes per day
milligrams per litre	mg/L	0.000 086 4 × L/s	tonne/d	tonnes per day
milligrams per litre	mg/L	0.01	tonne/ha-m	tonnes per hectare-metre
milligrams per litre	mg/L	0.001 36	ton/acre-ft	tons per acre-foot
milligrams per litre	mg/L	0.002 70 × cfs	ton/d	tons per day
parts per billion*	ppb	0.001 00	mg/L	milligrams per litre
parts per million*	ppm	0.999 70	mg/L	milligrams per litre
tonnes per day	tonne/d	408.734 52/cfs	mg/L	milligrams per litre
tonnes per day	tonne/d	11 574.074 07/ (L/s)	mg/L	milligrams per litre
tonnes per hectare-metre	tonne/ha-m	100	mg/L	milligrams per litre
tons per acre-foot	ton/acre-ft	735.466 76	mg/L	milligrams per litre
tons per day	ton/d	370.797 82/cfs	mg/L	milligrams per litre

*Assuming a density of pure water at 50°F

4.2 Temperature Conversions _____

Celsius: $°C = (5/9)(°F-32) = K-273.15 = AA-273$
Fahrenheit: $°F = (9/5)°C + 32 = (9/5)(K-273.15) + 32$
Kelvin: $K = °C + 273.15 = AA + 0.15 = (5/9)(°F-32) + 273.15$
Approximately Absolute: $AA = °C + 273 = K-0.15 = (5/9)(°F-32) + 273$
Rankine: $R = °F + 459.69$

4.3 Fahrenheit to Celsius

°F	°C	°F	°C	°F	°C	°F	°C
-40.0	-40.0	0.0	-17.8	40.0	4.4	80.0	26.7
-39.0	-39.4	1.0	-17.2	41.0	5.0	81.0	27.2
-38.0	-38.9	2.0	-16.7	42.0	5.6	82.0	27.8
-37.0	-38.3	3.0	-16.1	43.0	6.1	83.0	28.3
-36.0	-37.8	4.0	-15.6	44.0	6.7	84.0	28.9
-35.0	-37.2	5.0	-15.0	45.0	7.2	85.0	29.4
-34.0	-36.7	6.0	-14.4	46.0	7.8	86.0	30.0
-33.0	-36.1	7.0	-13.9	47.0	8.3	87.0	30.6
-32.0	-35.6	8.0	-13.3	48.0	8.9	88.0	31.1
-31.0	-35.0	9.0	-12.8	49.0	9.4	89.0	31.7
-30.0	-34.4	10.0	-12.2	50.0	10.0	90.0	32.2
-29.0	-33.9	11.0	-11.7	51.0	10.6	91.0	32.8
-28.0	-33.3	12.0	-11.1	52.0	11.1	92.0	33.3
-27.0	-32.8	13.0	-10.6	53.0	11.7	93.0	33.9
-26.0	-32.2	14.0	-10.0	54.0	12.2	94.0	34.4
-25.0	-31.7	15.0	-9.4	55.0	12.8	95.0	35.0
-24.0	-31.1	16.0	-8.9	56.0	13.3	96.0	35.6
-23.0	-30.6	17.0	-8.3	57.0	13.9	97.0	36.1
-22.0	-30.0	18.0	-7.8	58.0	14.4	98.0	36.7
-21.0	-29.4	19.0	-7.2	59.0	15.0	99.0	37.2
-20.0	-28.9	20.0	-6.7	60.0	15.6	100.0	37.8
-19.0	-28.3	21.0	-6.1	61.0	16.1	101.0	38.3
-18.0	-27.8	22.0	-5.6	62.0	16.7	102.0	38.9
-17.0	-27.2	23.0	-5.0	63.0	17.2	103.0	39.4
-16.0	-26.7	24.0	-4.4	64.0	17.8	104.0	40.0
-15.0	-26.1	25.0	-3.9	65.0	18.3	105.0	40.6
-14.0	-25.6	26.0	-3.3	66.0	18.9	106.0	41.1
-13.0	-25.0	27.0	-2.8	67.0	19.4	107.0	41.7
-12.0	-24.4	28.0	-2.2	68.0	20.0	108.0	42.2
-11.0	-23.9	29.0	-1.7	69.0	20.6	109.0	42.8
-10.0	-23.3	30.0	-1.1	70.0	21.1	110.0	43.3
-9.0	-22.8	31.0	-0.6	71.0	21.7	111.0	43.9
-8.0	-22.2	32.0	0.0	72.0	22.2	112.0	44.4
-7.0	-21.7	33.0	0.6	73.0	22.8	113.0	45.0
-6.0	-21.1	34.0	1.1	74.0	23.3	114.0	45.6
-5.0	-20.6	35.0	1.7	75.0	23.9	115.0	46.1
-4.0	-20.0	36.0	2.2	76.0	24.4	116.0	46.7
-3.0	-19.4	37.0	2.8	77.0	25.0	117.0	47.2
-2.0	-18.9	38.0	3.3	78.0	25.6	118.0	47.8
-1.0	-18.3	39.0	3.9	79.0	26.1	119.0	48.3

4.4 Celsius to Fahrenheit

°C	°F	°C	°F	°C	°F	°C	°F
-40.0	-40.0	-15.0	5.0	10.0	50.0	35.0	95.0
-39.0	-38.2	-14.0	6.8	11.0	51.8	36.0	96.8
-38.0	-36.4	-13.0	8.6	12.0	53.6	37.0	98.6
-37.0	-34.6	-12.0	10.4	13.0	55.4	38.0	100.4
-36.0	-32.8	-11.0	12.2	14.0	57.2	39.0	102.2
-35.0	-31.0	-10.0	14.0	15.0	59.0	40.0	104.0
-34.0	-29.2	-9.0	15.8	16.0	60.8	41.0	105.8
-33.0	-27.4	-8.0	17.6	17.0	62.6	42.0	107.6
-32.0	-25.6	-7.0	19.4	18.0	64.4	43.0	109.4
-31.0	-23.8	-6.0	21.2	19.0	66.2	44.0	111.2
-30.0	-22.0	-5.0	23.0	20.0	68.0	45.0	113.0
-29.0	-20.2	-4.0	24.8	21.0	69.8	46.0	114.8
-28.0	-18.4	-3.0	26.6	22.0	71.6	47.0	116.6
-27.0	-16.6	-2.0	28.4	23.0	73.4	48.0	118.4
-26.0	-14.8	-1.0	30.2	24.0	75.2	49.0	120.2
-25.0	-13.0	0.0	32.0	25.0	77.0	50.0	122.0
-24.0	-11.2	1.0	33.8	26.0	78.8	51.0	123.8
-23.0	-9.4	2.0	35.6	27.0	80.6	52.0	125.6
-22.0	-7.6	3.0	37.4	28.0	82.4	53.0	127.4
-21.0	-5.8	4.0	39.2	29.0	84.2	54.0	129.2
-20.0	-4.0	5.0	41.0	30.0	86.0	55.0	131.0
-19.0	-2.2	6.0	42.8	31.0	87.8	56.0	132.8
-18.0	-0.4	7.0	44.6	32.0	89.6	57.0	134.6
-17.0	1.4	8.0	46.4	33.0	91.4	58.0	136.4
-16.0	3.2	9.0	48.2	34.0	93.2	59.0	138.2
						60.0	140.0

4.5   Calendar Date to Julian Date (traditional year)

	Jan.	Feb.	Mar.	Apr.	May	June	July	Aug.	Sept.	Oct.	Nov.	Dec.
1	1	32	60	91	121	152	182	213	244	274	305	335
2	2	33	61	92	122	153	183	214	245	275	306	336
3	3	34	62	93	123	154	184	215	246	276	307	337
4	4	35	63	94	124	155	185	216	247	277	308	338
5	5	36	64	95	125	156	186	217	248	278	309	339
6	6	37	65	96	126	157	187	218	249	279	310	340
7	7	38	66	97	127	158	188	219	250	280	311	341
8	8	39	67	98	128	159	189	220	251	281	312	342
9	9	40	68	99	129	160	190	221	252	282	313	343
10	10	41	69	100	130	161	191	222	253	283	314	344
11	11	42	70	101	131	162	192	223	254	284	315	345
12	12	43	71	102	132	163	193	224	255	285	316	346
13	13	44	72	103	133	164	194	225	256	286	317	347
14	14	45	73	104	134	165	195	226	257	287	318	348
15	15	46	74	105	135	166	196	227	258	288	319	349
16	16	47	75	106	136	167	197	228	259	289	320	350
17	17	48	76	107	137	168	198	229	260	290	321	351
18	18	49	77	108	138	169	199	230	261	291	322	352
19	19	50	78	109	139	170	200	231	262	292	323	353
20	20	51	79	110	140	171	201	232	263	293	324	354
21	21	52	80	111	141	172	202	233	264	294	325	355
22	22	53	81	112	142	173	203	234	265	295	326	356
23	23	54	82	113	143	174	204	235	266	296	327	357
24	24	55	83	114	144	175	205	236	267	297	328	358
25	25	56	84	115	145	176	206	237	268	298	329	359
26	26	57	85	116	146	177	207	238	269	299	330	360
27	27	58	86	117	147	178	208	239	270	300	331	361
28	28	59	87	118	148	179	209	240	271	301	332	362
29	29	*	88	119	149	180	210	241	272	302	333	363
30	30		89	120	150	181	211	242	273	303	334	364
31	31		90		151		212	243		304		365

*In leap years add 1 to all dates after February 28.

4.6 Calendar Date to Julian Date (water year)

	Oct.	Nov.	Dec.	Jan.	Feb.	Mar.	Apr.	May	June	July	Aug.	Sept.
1	1	32	62	93	124	152	183	213	244	274	305	336
2	2	33	63	94	125	153	184	214	245	275	306	337
3	3	34	64	95	126	154	185	215	246	276	307	338
4	4	35	65	96	127	155	186	216	247	277	308	339
5	5	36	66	97	128	156	187	217	248	278	309	340
6	6	37	67	98	129	157	188	218	249	279	310	341
7	7	38	68	99	130	158	189	219	250	280	311	342
8	8	39	69	100	131	159	190	220	251	281	312	343
9	9	40	70	101	132	160	191	221	252	282	313	344
10	10	41	71	102	133	161	192	222	253	283	314	345
11	11	42	72	103	134	162	193	223	254	284	315	346
12	12	43	73	104	135	163	194	224	255	285	316	347
13	13	44	74	105	136	164	195	225	256	286	317	348
14	14	45	75	106	137	165	196	226	257	287	318	349
15	15	46	76	107	138	166	197	227	258	288	319	350
16	16	47	77	108	139	167	198	228	259	289	320	351
17	17	48	78	109	140	168	199	229	260	290	321	352
18	18	49	79	110	141	169	200	230	261	291	322	353
19	19	50	80	111	142	170	201	231	262	292	323	354
20	20	51	81	112	143	171	202	232	263	293	324	355
21	21	52	82	113	144	172	203	233	264	294	325	356
22	22	53	83	114	145	173	204	234	265	295	326	357
23	23	54	84	115	146	174	205	235	266	296	327	358
24	24	55	85	116	147	175	206	236	267	297	328	359
25	25	56	86	117	148	176	207	237	268	298	329	360
26	26	57	87	118	149	177	208	238	269	299	330	361
27	27	58	88	119	150	178	209	239	270	300	331	362
28	28	59	89	120	151	179	210	240	271	301	332	363
29	29	60	90	121	*	180	211	241	272	302	333	364
30	30	61	91	122		181	212	242	273	303	334	365
31	31		92	123		182		243		304	335	

*In leap years add 1 to all dates after February 28.

4.7   Inches to Decimals of a Foot

in.	0	⅛	¼	⅜	½	⅝	¾	⅞
0	0.000	0.010	0.021	0.031	0.042	0.052	0.063	0.073
1	0.083	0.094	0.104	0.115	0.125	0.135	0.146	0.156
2	0.167	0.177	0.188	0.198	0.208	0.219	0.229	0.240
3	0.250	0.260	0.271	0.281	0.292	0.302	0.313	0.323
4	0.333	0.344	0.354	0.365	0.375	0.385	0.396	0.406
5	0.417	0.427	0.438	0.448	0.458	0.469	0.479	0.490
6	0.500	0.510	0.521	0.531	0.542	0.552	0.563	0.573
7	0.583	0.594	0.604	0.615	0.625	0.635	0.646	0.656
8	0.667	0.677	0.688	0.698	0.708	0.719	0.729	0.740
9	0.750	0.760	0.771	0.781	0.792	0.802	0.813	0.823
10	0.833	0.844	0.854	0.865	0.875	0.885	0.896	0.906
11	0.917	0.927	0.938	0.948	0.958	0.969	0.979	0.990

4.8   Inch Fractions to Decimals and Millimetres

in.	decimal	mm	in.	decimal	mm
1/64	0.016	0.397	33/64	0.516	13.097
1/32	0.031	0.794	17/32	0.531	13.494
3/64	0.047	1.191	35/64	0.547	13.891
1/16	0.063	1.588	9/16	0.563	14.288
5/64	0.078	1.984	37/64	0.578	14.684
3/32	0.094	2.381	19/32	0.594	15.081
7/64	0.109	2.778	39/64	0.609	15.478
1/8	0.125	3.175	5/8	0.625	15.875
9/64	0.141	3.572	41/64	0.641	16.272
5/32	0.156	3.969	21/32	0.656	16.669
11/64	0.172	4.366	43/64	0.672	17.066
3/16	0.188	4.763	11/16	0.688	17.463
13/64	0.203	5.159	45/64	0.703	17.859
7/32	0.219	5.556	23/32	0.719	18.256
15/64	0.234	5.953	47/64	0.734	18.653
1/4	0.250	6.350	3/4	0.750	19.050
17/64	0.266	6.747	49/64	0.766	19.447
9/32	0.281	7.144	25/32	0.781	19.844
19/64	0.297	7.541	51/64	0.797	20.241
5/16	0.313	7.938	13/16	0.813	20.638
21/64	0.328	8.334	53/64	0.828	21.034
11/32	0.344	8.731	27/32	0.844	21.431
23/64	0.359	9.128	55/64	0.859	21.828
3/8	0.375	9.525	7/8	0.875	22.225
25/64	0.391	9.922	57/64	0.891	22.622
13/32	0.406	10.319	29/32	0.906	23.019
27/64	0.422	10.716	59/64	0.922	23.416
7/16	0.438	11.113	15/16	0.938	23.812
29/64	0.453	11.509	61/64	0.953	24.209
15/32	0.469	11.906	31/32	0.969	24.606
31/64	0.484	12.303	63/64	0.984	25.003
1/2	0.500	12.700	1	1.000	25.400

5

Mensuration Formulas and Tables

5.1   Areas and Volumes of Geometric Shapes

Shape	Area	Figure Reference
circle	πr^2	3a
circle segment	$\frac{1}{2} r^2 ([\pi\alpha/180] - \sin \alpha)$	3b
circle sector	$\pi r^2 \alpha/360$	3c
ellipse	πab	3d
parabola	$\frac{4}{3} xy$	3e
rectangle	ab	3f
parallelogram	ah	3g
rhombus	$\frac{1}{2}$ pq	3h
equilateral triangle	$\frac{1}{4} a^2 \sqrt{3}$	3i
right triangle	$\frac{1}{2} ab$	3j
general triangle	$\frac{1}{2} hc$	3k
trapezoid	$\frac{1}{2} h (a + b)$	3l
polygons	$\frac{1}{4} ns^2 \cot (180/n)$ Where n = number of sides	3m
quadrilateral, general	$\frac{1}{2} pq \sin \theta = \frac{1}{4} (b^2 + d^2 - a^2 - c^2) \tan \theta$	3n

Shape	Volume	Figure Reference
cube	abc	4a
wedge, parallelogram face	$\frac{1}{6} dh (2a + b)$	4b
pyramid	$\frac{1}{3} abh$	4c
prismatoid	$\frac{1}{6} h(B_1 + 4M + B_2)$ Where: $B_1 = cd$, $B_2 = ab$, and $M = ([a + c]/2) ([b + d]/2)$	4d
wedge, triangular face	$\frac{1}{6} ab (2L_1 + L_2)$	4e
cone	$\frac{1}{3} Bh$ Where: $B = \pi r^2$	4f
cone frustrum	$\frac{1}{3} h (B_1 + B_2 + \sqrt{B_1 B_2})$ Where: $B_1 = \pi r_1^2$ and $B_2 = \pi r_2^2$	4g
hemisphere of cone frustrum	$\frac{1}{6} h (B_1 + B_2 + \sqrt{B_1 B_2})$ Where: $B_1 = \pi r_1^2$ and $B_2 = \pi r_2^2$	4h
sphere	$\frac{4}{3} \pi r^3$	4i
sphere segment of one base	$\frac{1}{3} \pi h^2 (3r - h)$	4j
sphere segment of two bases	$\frac{1}{6} \pi h(3a^2 + 3b^2 + h^2)$	4k
cylinder	$\pi r^2 h$	4l
elliptic tank	$\pi r_1 r_2 h$	4m
elliptic sinusoid	$4abD(1 - 2/\pi)$	4n
gully check	$\frac{1}{12} \pi abh$	4o
prairie dugout	$\frac{5}{24} ah \sqrt{3} (L_1 - L_2)$	4p
elliptic depression	$\frac{4}{9} \pi abh$	4q
pit reservoir	$(h/12) (4aL_1 + 2aL_2 - hL_1)$	4r
gully check, trapezoidal face	$(h/12) (2aL_1 + 2aL_2 - hL_1)$	4s
cat scoop	$\frac{1}{2} ahL$	4t
trough	$\frac{1}{2} hL (480h - a)$ Assumes: h = radius/2	4u

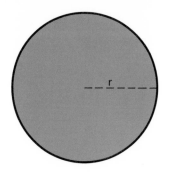

$A = \pi r^2$

Figure 3a   Circle

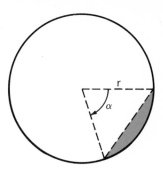

$A = \frac{1}{2}r^2 \left([\pi\alpha/180] - \sin \alpha \right)$

Figure 3b   Circle Segment

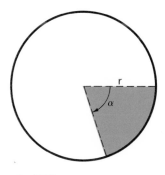

$A = \pi r^2 \alpha/360$

Figure 3c   Circle Sector

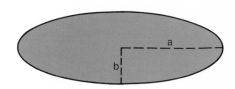

$A = \pi ab$

Figure 3d   Ellipse

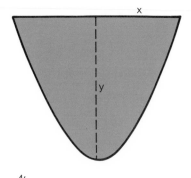

$A = \frac{4}{3}xy$

Figure 3e   Parabola

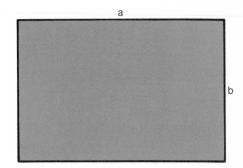

$A = ab$

Figure 3f   Rectangle

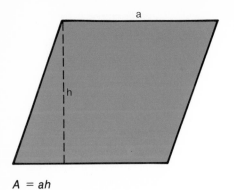

$A = ah$

Figure 3g   Parallelogram

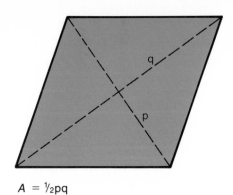

$A = \tfrac{1}{2}pq$

Figure 3h   Rhombus

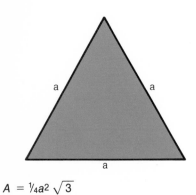

$A = \tfrac{1}{4}a^2 \sqrt{3}$

Figure 3i   Equilateral Triangle

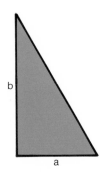

$A = \tfrac{1}{2}ab$

Figure 3j   Right Triangle

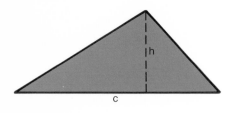

$A = \tfrac{1}{2}hc$

Figure 3k   General Triangle

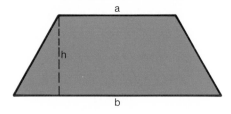

$A = \tfrac{1}{2}h\,(a + b)$

Figure 3l   Trapezoid

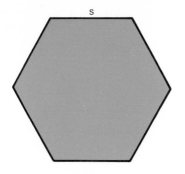

$A = \frac{1}{4}ns^2 \cot (180/n)$
Where n = number of sides

Figure 3m Polygons

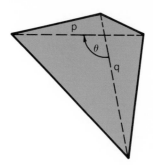

$A = \frac{1}{2}pq \sin \theta = \frac{1}{4}(b^2 + d^2 - a^2 - c^2)$
$\tan \theta$

Figure 3n Quadrilateral, General

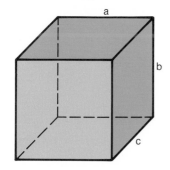

$V = abc$

Figure 4a Cube

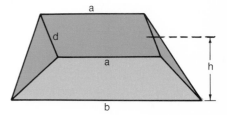

$V = \frac{1}{6}dh\,(2a + b)$

Figure 4b Wedge, Parallelogram Face

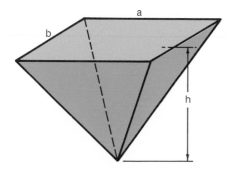

$V = \frac{1}{3}abh$

Figure 4c Pyramid

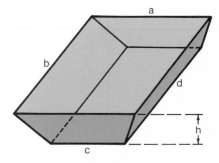

$V = \frac{1}{6}h(B_1 + 4M + B_2)$
Where: $B_1 = cd$, $B_2 = ab$, and
$M = (|a + c|/2)\,(|b + d|/2)$

Figure 4d Prismatoid

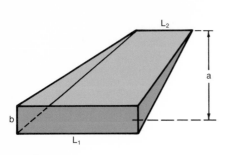

$V = \frac{1}{6}ab\,(2L_1 + L_2)$

Figure 4e   Wedge, Triangular Face

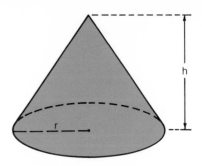

$V = \frac{1}{3}Bh$ Where: $B = \pi r^2$

Figure 4f   Cone

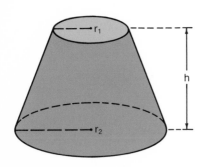

$V = \frac{1}{3}h\,(B_1 + B_2 + \sqrt{B_1\,B_2})$
Where: $B_1 = \pi r_1^2$ and $B_2 = \pi r_2^2$

Figure 4g   Cone Frustrum

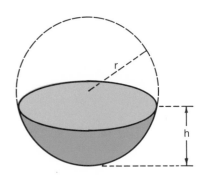

$V = \frac{1}{6}h\,(B_1 + B_2 + \sqrt{B_1\,B_2})$
Where: $B_1 = \pi r_1^2$ and $B_2 = \pi r_2^2$

Figure 4h   Hemisphere of Cone Frustrum

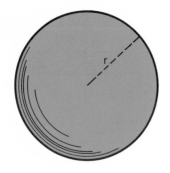

$V = \frac{4}{3}\pi r^3$

Figure 4i   Sphere

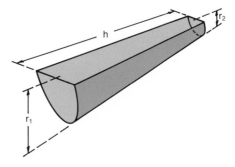

$V = \frac{1}{3}\pi h^2\,(3r - h)$

Figure 4j   Sphere Segment of One Base

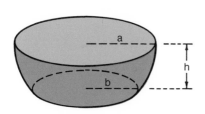

$V = \frac{1}{6}\pi h(3a^2 + 3b^2 + h^2)$

Figure 4k Sphere Segment of Two Bases

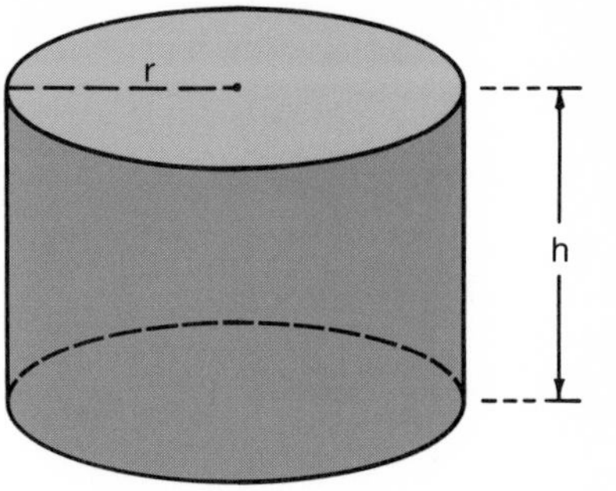

$V = \pi r^2 h$

Figure 4l Cylinder

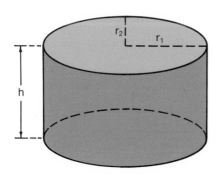

$V = \pi r_1 r_2 h$

Figure 4m Elliptic Tank

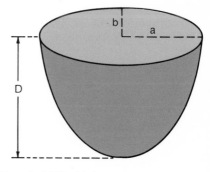

$V = 4abD(1 - 2/\pi)$

Figure 4n Elliptic Sinusoid

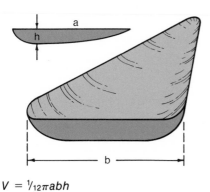

$V = \frac{1}{12}\pi abh$

Figure 4o Gully Check

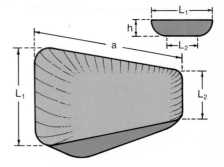

$V = \frac{5}{24}ah\sqrt{3}\,(L_1 - L_2)$

Figure 4p Prairie Dugout

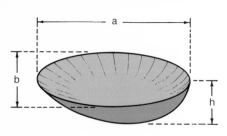

$V = {}^{4}/_{9}\pi abh$

Figure 4q   Elliptic Depression

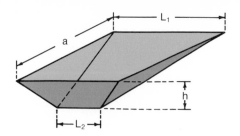

$V = (h/12)\,(4aL_1 + 2aL_2 - hL_1)$

Figure 4r   Pit Reservoir

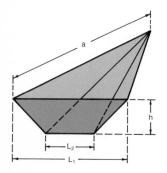

$V = (h/12)\,(2aL_1 + 2aL_2 - hL_1)$

Figure 4s   Gully Check, Trapezoidal Face

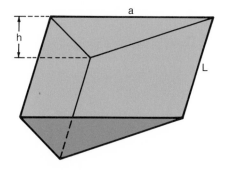

$V = {}^{1}/_{2}ahL$

Figure 4t   Cat Scoop

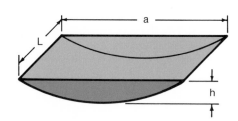

$V = {}^{1}/_{2}hL\,(480h - a)$ Assumes: h = radius/2

Figure 4u   Trough

5.2 Capacities of Cylindrical Tanks

Inside Diameter in.	Gallons per Inch Depth	Inside Diameter ft	Gallons per Inch Depth
12	0.49	5	12.24
13	0.57	6	17.63
14	0.67	7	23.99
15	0.76	8	31.33
16	0.87	9	39.66
17	0.98	10	48.96
18	1.10	11	59.24
19	1.23	12	70.50
20	1.36	13	82.74
21	1.50	14	95.96
22	1.65	15	110.16
23	1.80	16	125.34
24	1.96	17	141.49
25	2.12	18	158.63
26	2.30	19	176.75
27	2.48	20	195.84
28	2.67	21	215.91
29	2.86	22	236.97
30	3.06	23	259.00
31	3.27	24	282.01
32	3.48	25	306.00
33	3.70	26	330.97
34	3.93	27	356.92
35	4.16	28	383.85
36	4.41	29	411.75
37	4.65	30	440.64
38	4.91	31	470.50
39	5.17	32	501.35
40	5.44	33	533.17
41	5.72	34	565.98
42	6.00	35	599.76
43	6.29	36	634.52
44	6.58	37	670.26
45	6.88	38	706.98
46	7.19	39	744.68
47	7.51	40	783.36
48	7.83	41	823.02
49	8.16	42	863.65
50	8.50	43	905.27
51	8.84	44	947.86
52	9.19	45	991.44
53	9.55	46	1035.99
54	9.91	47	1081.52
55	10.28	48	1128.04
56	10.66	49	1175.53
57	11.05	50	1224.00
58	11.44		
59	11.84		
60	12.24		

5.3   Volume of Various Diameter Pipe

Actual Inside Diameter in.	Gallons in One Lineal Foot	Actual Inside Diameter in.	Gallons in One Lineal Foot	Actual Inside Diameter in.	Gallons in One Lineal Foot
0.125	0.001	5.125	1.072	10.125	4.183
0.250	0.003	5.250	1.125	10.250	4.287
0.375	0.006	5.375	1.179	10.375	4.392
0.500	0.010	5.500	1.234	10.500	4.498
0.625	0.016	5.625	1.291	10.625	4.606
0.750	0.023	5.750	1.349	10.750	4.715
0.875	0.031	5.875	1.408	10.875	4.825
1.000	0.041	6.000	1.469	11.000	4.937
1.125	0.052	6.125	1.531	11.125	5.050
1.250	0.064	6.250	1.594	11.250	5.164
1.375	0.077	6.375	1.658	11.375	5.279
1.500	0.092	6.500	1.724	11.500	5.396
1.625	0.108	6.625	1.791	11.625	5.514
1.750	0.125	6.750	1.859	11.750	5.633
1.875	0.143	6.875	1.928	11.875	5.753
2.000	0.163	7.000	1.999	12.000	5.875
2.125	0.184	7.125	2.071	12.125	5.998
2.250	0.207	7.250	2.145	12.250	6.123
2.375	0.230	7.375	2.219	12.375	6.248
2.500	0.255	7.500	2.295	12.500	6.375
2.625	0.281	7.625	2.372	12.625	6.503
2.750	0.309	7.750	2.451	12.750	6.633
2.875	0.337	7.875	2.530	12.875	6.763
3.000	0.367	8.000	2.611	13.000	6.895
3.125	0.398	8.125	2.693	13.125	7.028
3.250	0.431	8.250	2.777	13.250	7.163
3.375	0.465	8.375	2.862	13.375	7.299
3.500	0.500	8.500	2.948	13.500	7.436
3.625	0.536	8.625	3.035	13.625	7.574
3.750	0.574	8.750	3.124	13.750	7.714
3.875	0.613	8.875	3.214	13.875	7.855
4.000	0.653	9.000	3.305	14.000	7.997
4.125	0.694	9.125	3.397	14.125	8.140
4.250	0.737	9.250	3.491	14.250	8.285
4.375	0.781	9.375	3.586	14.375	8.431
4.500	0.826	9.500	3.682	14.500	8.578
4.625	0.873	9.625	3.780	14.625	8.727
4.750	0.921	9.750	3.879	14.750	8.877
4.875	0.970	9.875	3.979	14.875	9.028
5.000	1.020	10.000	4.080	15.000	9.180

5.4 Road Surface Acreages

Road Width	Surface Area		
ft	acres/mi	acres/1000 ft	ha/km
8	0.97	0.18	0.24
9	1.09	0.21	0.27
10	1.21	0.23	0.30
11	1.33	0.25	0.34
12	1.45	0.28	0.37
13	1.58	0.30	0.40
14	1.70	0.32	0.43
15	1.82	0.34	0.46
16	1.94	0.37	0.49
17	2.06	0.39	0.52
18	2.18	0.41	0.55
19	2.30	0.44	0.58
20	2.42	0.46	0.61
21	2.55	0.48	0.64
22	2.67	0.51	0.67
23	2.79	0.53	0.70
24	2.91	0.55	0.73
25	3.03	0.57	0.76
26	3.15	0.60	0.79
27	3.27	0.62	0.82
28	3.39	0.64	0.85
29	3.52	0.67	0.88
30	3.64	0.69	0.91
35	4.24	0.80	1.07
40	4.85	0.92	1.22
45	5.45	1.03	1.37
50	6.06	1.15	1.52
55	6.67	1.26	1.68
60	7.27	1.38	1.83
65	7.88	1.49	1.98
70	8.48	1.61	2.13
75	9.09	1.72	2.29
80	9.70	1.84	2.44
85	10.30	1.95	2.59
90	10.91	2.07	2.74
95	11.52	2.18	2.90
100	12.12	2.30	3.05
110	13.33	2.53	3.35
120	14.55	2.75	3.66
130	15.76	2.98	3.96
140	16.97	3.21	4.27
150	18.18	3.44	4.57
160	19.39	3.67	4.88
170	20.61	3.90	5.18
180	21.82	4.13	5.49
190	23.03	4.36	5.79
200	24.24	4.59	6.10

6

Drainage Basin Morphometric Formulas

6.1   Mean Basin Slope

(Method 1) $S_b = \dfrac{CI \times \Sigma \text{ (length of contours)}}{A}$

(Method 2) $S_b = \dfrac{(\text{elev. at } 0.85L) - (\text{elev. at } 0.10L)}{0.75L}$

(Method 3) $S_b = \dfrac{CI \times \text{(length of contour belt)}}{(\text{area of contour belt})}$

Where: S_b = mean basin slope in ft/mi
CI = the contour interval in ft
L = the length of the longest channel extended from the basin mouth to the drainage divide in mi
A = the basin area in mi²
All other lengths in mi, elevations in ft, and areas in mi².

6.2   Bifurcation Ratio

$$R_b = \frac{N_u}{N_{u+1}}$$

Where: N_u = the number of stream segments of a given stream order
N_{u+1} = the number of segments of the next highest stream order.

6.3   Circularity Ratio

$$R_c = \frac{A}{A_c}$$

Where: A = the basin area
A_c = the area of a circle having the same perimeter as the basin.

6.4 Constant of Channel Maintenance

$$C = \frac{1}{D_d}$$

Where: D_d (drainage density) =

$$D_d = \frac{\Sigma l_u}{A}$$

Where: Σl_u = the sum of the lengths of each stream segment of each order, u
A = the basin area.

6.5 Form Factor

$$F = \frac{A}{L^2}$$

Where: A and L are as defined in Sec. 6.1.

6.6 Relief Ratio

$$R_h = \frac{H}{L}$$

Where: H = the total relief of the basin
L is as defined in Sec. 6.1.

6.7 Stream Frequency

$$F_s = \frac{\Sigma N_u}{A}$$

Where: ΣN_u = the sum of the numbers of all stream segments of all orders
A is as defined in Sec. 6.1.

7

Topographic, Cartographic, and Photogrammetric Tables

7.1   Slope Conversions (Percent–Degrees–Ratio)

Percent	Degrees	Ratio	Percent	Degrees	Ratio
1	0.57	100.0:1	51	27.02	1.96:1
2	1.15	50.0:1	52	27.47	1.92:1
3	1.72	33.3:1	53	27.92	1.89:1
4	2.29	25.0:1	54	28.37	1.85:1
5	2.86	20.0:1	55	28.81	1.82:1
6	3.43	16.7:1	56	29.25	1.79:1
7	4.00	14.3:1	57	29.68	1.75:1
8	4.57	12.5:1	58	30.11	1.72:1
9	5.14	11.1:1	59	30.54	1.69:1
10	5.71	10.0:1	60	30.96	1.67:1
11	6.28	9.1:1	61	31.38	1.64:1
12	6.84	8.3:1	62	31.80	1.61:1
13	7.41	7.7:1	63	32.21	1.59:1
14	7.97	7.1:1	64	32.62	1.56:1
15	8.53	6.7:1	65	33.02	1.54:1
16	9.09	6.3:1	66	33.42	1.52:1
17	9.65	5.9:1	67	33.82	1.49:1
18	10.20	5.6:1	68	34.22	1.47:1
19	10.76	5.3:1	69	34.61	1.45:1
20	11.31	5.0:1	70	34.99	1.43:1
21	11.86	4.8:1	71	35.37	1.41:1
22	12.41	4.5:1	72	35.75	1.39:1
23	12.95	4.3:1	73	36.13	1.37:1
24	13.50	4.2:1	74	36.50	1.35:1
25	14.04	4.0:1	75	36.87	1.33:1
26	14.57	3.8:1	76	37.23	1.32:1
27	15.11	3.7:1	77	37.60	1.30:1
28	15.64	3.6:1	78	37.95	1.28:1
29	16.17	3.4:1	79	38.31	1.27:1
30	16.70	3.3:1	80	38.66	1.25:1
31	17.22	3.2:1	81	39.01	1.23:1
32	17.74	3.1:1	82	39.35	1.22:1
33	18.26	3.0:1	83	39.69	1.20:1
34	18.78	2.9:1	84	40.03	1.19:1
35	19.29	2.9:1	85	40.36	1.18:1
36	19.80	2.8:1	86	40.70	1.16:1
37	20.30	2.7:1	87	41.02	1.15:1
38	20.81	2.6:1	88	41.35	1.14:1
39	21.31	2.6:1	89	41.67	1.12:1
40	21.80	2.5:1	90	41.99	1.11:1
41	22.29	2.4:1	91	42.30	1.10:1
42	22.78	2.4:1	92	42.61	1.09:1
43	23.27	2.3:1	93	42.92	1.08:1
44	23.75	2.3:1	94	43.23	1.06:1
45	24.23	2.2:1	95	43.53	1.05:1
46	24.70	2.2:1	96	43.83	1.04:1
47	25.17	2.1:1	97	44.13	1.03:1
48	25.64	2.1:1	98	44.42	1.02:1
49	26.10	2.0:1	99	44.71	1.01:1
50	26.57	2.0:1	100	45.00	1.00:1

7.2 Slope Conversions (Slope–ft/mi–in./100 ft)

Slope	ft/mi	in./100 ft	Slope	ft/mi	in./100 ft
0.001	5.28	1.2	0.051	269.28	61.2
0.002	10.56	2.4	0.052	274.56	62.4
0.003	15.84	3.6	0.053	279.84	63.6
0.004	21.12	4.8	0.054	285.12	64.8
0.005	26.40	6.0	0.055	290.40	66.0
0.006	31.68	7.2	0.056	295.68	67.2
0.007	36.96	8.4	0.057	300.96	68.4
0.008	42.24	9.6	0.058	306.24	69.6
0.009	47.52	10.8	0.059	311.52	70.8
0.010	52.80	12.0	0.060	316.80	72.0
0.011	58.08	13.2	0.061	322.08	73.2
0.012	63.36	14.4	0.062	327.36	74.4
0.013	68.64	15.6	0.063	332.64	75.6
0.014	73.92	16.8	0.064	337.92	76.8
0.015	79.20	18.0	0.065	343.20	78.0
0.016	84.48	19.2	0.066	348.48	79.2
0.017	89.76	20.4	0.067	353.76	80.4
0.018	95.04	21.6	0.068	359.04	81.6
0.019	100.32	22.8	0.069	364.32	82.8
0.020	105.60	24.0	0.070	369.60	84.0
0.021	110.88	25.2	0.071	374.88	85.2
0.022	116.16	26.4	0.072	380.16	86.4
0.023	121.44	27.6	0.073	385.44	87.6
0.024	126.72	28.8	0.074	390.72	88.8
0.025	132.00	30.0	0.075	396.00	90.0
0.026	137.28	31.2	0.076	401.28	91.2
0.027	142.56	32.4	0.077	406.56	92.4
0.028	147.84	33.6	0.078	411.84	93.6
0.029	153.12	34.8	0.079	417.12	94.8
0.030	158.40	36.0	0.080	422.40	96.0
0.031	163.68	37.2	0.081	427.68	97.2
0.032	168.96	38.4	0.082	432.96	98.4
0.033	174.24	39.6	0.083	438.24	99.6
0.034	179.52	40.8	0.084	443.52	100.8
0.035	184.80	42.0	0.085	448.80	102.0
0.036	190.08	43.2	0.086	454.08	103.2
0.037	195.36	44.4	0.087	459.36	104.4
0.038	200.64	45.6	0.088	464.64	105.6
0.039	205.92	46.8	0.089	469.92	106.8
0.040	211.20	48.0	0.090	475.20	108.0
0.041	216.48	49.2	0.091	480.48	109.2
0.042	221.76	50.4	0.092	485.76	110.4
0.043	227.04	51.6	0.093	491.04	111.6
0.044	232.32	52.8	0.094	496.32	112.8
0.045	237.60	54.0	0.095	501.60	114.0
0.046	242.88	55.2	0.096	506.88	115.2
0.047	248.16	56.4	0.097	512.16	116.4
0.048	253.44	57.6	0.098	517.44	117.6
0.049	258.72	58.8	0.099	522.72	118.8
0.050	264.00	60.0	0.100	528.00	120.0

7.2 Slope Conversions (Slope–ft/mi–in./100 ft) (continued)

Slope	ft/mi	in./100 ft	Slope	ft/mi	in./100 ft
0.101	533.28	121.2	0.151	797.28	181.2
0.102	538.56	122.4	0.152	802.56	182.4
0.103	543.84	123.6	0.153	807.84	183.6
0.104	549.12	124.8	0.154	813.12	184.8
0.105	554.40	126.0	0.155	818.40	186.0
0.106	559.68	127.2	0.156	823.68	187.2
0.107	564.96	128.4	0.157	828.96	188.4
0.108	570.24	129.6	0.158	834.24	189.6
0.109	575.52	130.8	0.159	839.52	190.8
0.110	580.80	132.0	0.160	844.80	192.0
0.111	586.08	133.2	0.161	850.08	193.2
0.112	591.36	134.4	0.162	855.36	194.4
0.113	596.64	135.6	0.163	860.64	195.6
0.114	601.92	136.8	0.164	865.92	196.8
0.115	607.20	138.0	0.165	871.20	198.0
0.116	612.48	139.2	0.166	876.48	199.2
0.117	617.76	140.4	0.167	881.76	200.4
0.118	623.04	141.6	0.168	887.04	201.6
0.119	628.32	142.8	0.169	892.32	202.8
0.120	633.60	144.0	0.170	897.60	204.0
0.121	638.88	145.2	0.171	902.88	205.2
0.122	644.16	146.4	0.172	908.16	206.4
0.123	649.44	147.6	0.173	913.44	207.6
0.124	654.72	148.8	0.174	918.72	208.8
0.125	660.00	150.0	0.175	924.00	210.0
0.126	665.28	151.2	0.176	929.28	211.2
0.127	670.56	152.4	0.177	934.56	212.4
0.128	675.84	153.6	0.178	939.84	213.6
0.129	681.12	154.8	0.179	945.12	214.8
0.130	686.40	156.0	0.180	950.40	216.0
0.131	691.68	157.2	0.181	955.68	217.2
0.132	696.96	158.4	0.182	960.96	218.4
0.133	702.24	159.6	0.183	966.24	219.6
0.134	707.52	160.8	0.184	971.52	220.8
0.135	712.80	162.0	0.185	976.80	222.0
0.136	718.08	163.2	0.186	982.08	223.2
0.137	723.36	164.4	0.187	987.36	224.4
0.138	728.64	165.6	0.188	992.64	225.6
0.139	733.92	166.8	0.189	997.92	226.8
0.140	739.20	168.0	0.190	1003.20	228.0
0.141	744.48	169.2	0.191	1008.48	229.2
0.142	749.76	170.4	0.192	1013.76	230.4
0.143	755.04	171.6	0.193	1019.04	231.6
0.144	760.32	172.8	0.194	1024.32	232.8
0.145	765.60	174.0	0.195	1029.60	234.0
0.146	770.88	175.2	0.196	1034.88	235.2
0.147	776.16	176.4	0.197	1040.16	236.4
0.148	781.44	177.6	0.198	1045.44	237.6
0.149	786.72	178.8	0.199	1050.72	238.8
0.150	792.00	180.0	0.200	1056.00	240.0

7.2 Slope Conversions (Slope–ft/mi–in./100 ft) (continued)

Slope	ft/mi	in./100 ft	Slope	ft/mi	in./100 ft
0.201	1061.28	241.2	0.251	1325.28	301.2
0.202	1066.56	242.4	0.252	1330.56	302.4
0.203	1071.84	243.6	0.253	1335.84	303.6
0.204	1077.12	244.8	0.254	1341.12	304.8
0.205	1082.40	246.0	0.255	1346.40	306.0
0.206	1087.68	247.2	0.256	1351.68	307.2
0.207	1092.96	248.4	0.257	1356.96	308.4
0.208	1098.24	249.6	0.258	1362.24	309.6
0.209	1103.52	250.8	0.259	1367.52	310.8
0.210	1108.80	252.0	0.260	1372.80	312.0
0.211	1114.08	253.2	0.261	1378.08	313.2
0.212	1119.36	254.4	0.262	1383.36	314.4
0.213	1124.64	255.6	0.263	1388.64	315.6
0.214	1129.92	256.8	0.264	1393.92	316.8
0.215	1135.20	258.0	0.265	1399.20	318.0
0.216	1140.48	259.2	0.266	1404.48	319.2
0.217	1145.76	260.4	0.267	1409.76	320.4
0.218	1151.04	261.6	0.268	1415.04	321.6
0.219	1156.32	262.8	0.269	1420.32	322.8
0.220	1161.60	264.0	0.270	1425.60	324.0
0.221	1166.88	265.2	0.271	1430.88	325.2
0.222	1172.16	266.4	0.272	1436.16	326.4
0.223	1177.44	267.6	0.273	1441.44	327.6
0.224	1182.72	268.8	0.274	1446.72	328.8
0.225	1188.00	270.0	0.275	1452.00	330.0
0.226	1193.28	271.2	0.276	1457.28	331.2
0.227	1198.56	272.4	0.277	1462.56	332.4
0.228	1203.84	273.6	0.278	1467.84	333.6
0.229	1209.12	274.8	0.279	1473.12	334.8
0.230	1214.40	276.0	0.280	1478.40	336.0
0.231	1219.68	277.2	0.281	1483.68	337.2
0.232	1224.96	278.4	0.282	1488.96	338.4
0.233	1230.24	279.6	0.283	1494.24	339.6
0.234	1235.52	280.8	0.284	1499.52	340.8
0.235	1240.80	282.0	0.285	1504.80	342.0
0.236	1246.08	283.2	0.286	1510.08	343.2
0.237	1251.36	284.4	0.287	1515.36	344.4
0.238	1256.64	285.6	0.288	1520.64	345.6
0.239	1261.92	286.8	0.289	1525.92	346.8
0.240	1267.20	288.0	0.290	1531.20	348.0
0.241	1272.48	289.2	0.291	1536.48	349.2
0.242	1277.76	290.4	0.292	1541.76	350.4
0.243	1283.04	291.6	0.293	1547.04	351.6
0.244	1288.32	292.8	0.294	1552.32	352.8
0.245	1293.60	294.0	0.295	1557.60	354.0
0.246	1298.88	295.2	0.296	1562.88	355.2
0.247	1304.16	296.4	0.297	1568.16	356.4
0.248	1309.44	297.6	0.298	1573.44	357.6
0.249	1314.72	298.8	0.299	1578.72	358.8
0.250	1320.00	300.0	0.300	1584.00	360.0

7.3 Map and Photograph Scale Conversions

Ratio	in./mi	mi/in.	mi²/in.²	cm/km	km/cm	km²/cm²
1:100 000 0	0.06	15.783	249.098	0.10	10.000	100.000
1:500 000	0.13	7.891	62.274	0.20	5.000	25.000
1:420 000	0.15	6.629	43.941	0.24	4.200	17.640
1:250 000	0.25	3.946	15.569	0.40	2.500	6.250
1:126 720	0.50	2.000	4.000	0.79	1.267	1.606
1:125 000	0.51	1.973	3.892	0.80	1.250	1.563
1:120 000	0.53	1.894	3.587	0.83	1.200	1.440
1:110 000	0.58	1.736	3.014	0.91	1.100	1.210
1:100 000	0.63	1.578	2.491	1.00	1.000	1.000
1:900 00	0.70	1.420	2.018	1.11	0.900	0.810
1:800 00	0.79	1.263	1.594	1.25	0.800	0.640
1:633 60	1.00	1.000	1.000	1.58	0.634	0.401
1:625 00	1.01	0.986	0.973	1.60	0.625	0.391
1:580 00	1.09	0.915	0.838	1.72	0.580	0.336
1:500 00	1.27	0.789	0.623	2.00	0.500	0.250
1:450 00	1.41	0.710	0.504	2.22	0.450	0.203
1:316 80	2.00	0.500	0.250	3.16	0.317	0.100
1:300 00	2.11	0.473	0.224	3.33	0.300	0.090
1:240 00	2.64	0.379	0.143	4.17	0.240	0.058
1:200 00	3.17	0.316	0.100	5.00	0.200	0.040
1:158 40	4.00	0.250	0.063	6.31	0.158	0.025
1:120 00	5.28	0.189	0.036	8.33	0.120	0.014
1:105 60	6.00	0.167	0.028	9.47	0.106	0.011
1:100 00	6.34	0.158	0.025	10.00	0.100	0.010
1:9600	6.60	0.152	0.023	10.42	0.096	0.009
1:7920	8.00	0.125	0.016	12.63	0.079	0.006
1:6400	9.90	0.101	0.010	15.63	0.064	0.004
1:6000	10.56	0.095	0.009	16.67	0.060	0.004
1:5280	12.00	0.083	0.007	18.94	0.053	0.003
1:5000	12.67	0.079	0.006	20.00	0.050	0.003
1:4600	13.77	0.073	0.005	21.74	0.046	0.002
1:4200	15.09	0.066	0.004	23.81	0.042	0.002
1:4000	15.84	0.063	0.004	25.00	0.040	0.002
1:3200	19.80	0.051	0.003	31.25	0.032	0.001
1:2400	26.40	0.038	0.001	41.67	0.024	0.001
1:1584	40.00	0.025	0.001	63.13	0.016	2.5×10^{-4}
1:1500	42.24	0.024	0.001	66.67	0.015	2.3×10^{-4}
1:1200	52.80	0.019	3.6×10^{-4}	83.33	0.012	1.4×10^{-4}
1:1000	63.36	0.016	2.5×10^{-4}	100.00	0.010	1.0×10^{-4}
1:800	79.20	0.013	1.6×10^{-4}	125.00	0.008	6.4×10^{-5}
1:600	105.60	0.009	9.0×10^{-5}	166.67	0.006	3.6×10^{-5}
1:500	126.72	0.008	6.2×10^{-5}	200.00	0.005	2.5×10^{-5}
1:250	253.44	0.004	1.6×10^{-5}	400.00	0.003	6.3×10^{-6}
1:200	316.80	0.003	1.0×10^{-5}	500.00	0.002	4.0×10^{-6}

8

Physical Constants

8.1   Density and Weight of Water

Density of water at 50°F (10°C) is equal to 0.999 701 g/cm^3
1 ft^3 of water at 50°F (10°C) weighs 62.409 31 lb
1 ft^3 of water is equal to 7.480 52 gal
1 gal of water at 50°F (10°C) weighs 8.342 91 lb
1 m^3 of water at 50°F (10°C) weighs 999.701 kg
1 in. of rain falling on 1 acre is equal to 27 154 gal and weighs 113.3 ton
1 ft^3 of ice at 32°F (0°C) weighs 57.264 80 lb

8.2   Density of Water at Various Temperatures

Temp °C	Density g/cm^3	Density lb/ft^3	Temp °C	Density g/cm^3	Density lb/ft^3
0	0.99984	62.41797	21	0.99800	62.30310
1	0.99990	62.42172	22	0.99777	62.28875
2	0.99994	62.42421	23	0.99754	62.27439
3	0.99997	62.42609	24	0.99730	62.25941
4	0.99997	62.42609	25	0.99705	62.24380
5	0.99996	62.42546	26	0.99679	62.22757
6	0.99994	62.42421	27	0.99652	62.21071
7	0.99990	62.42172	28	0.99624	62.19323
8	0.99985	62.41860	29	0.99595	62.17513
9	0.99978	62.41423	30	0.99565	62.15640
10	0.99970	62.40929	31	0.99535	62.13767
11	0.99961	62.40361	32	0.99503	62.11769
12	0.99950	62.39675	33	0.99471	62.09772
13	0.99938	62.38926	34	0.99438	62.07712
14	0.99925	62.38114	35	0.99404	62.05589
15	0.99910	62.37178	36	0.99369	62.03404
16	0.99895	62.36241	37	0.99333	62.01157
17	0.99878	62.35180	38	0.99297	61.98909
18	0.99860	62.34056	39	0.99260	61.96599
19	0.99841	62.32870	40	0.99222	61.94227
20	0.99821	62.31621			

8.3   Density of Common Fluids

Fluid	Temperature °C	Density g/cm^3	Density lb/ft^3
Alcohol, ethyl	20	0.791	49.4
Alcohol, methyl	0	0.810	50.6
Brine	0	1.20	74.9
Gasoline	25	0.70	43.7
Pure water	3.98	1.00	62.4
Sea water	15	1.025	64.0

8.4   Specific Gravity and Density of Common Solids

Solid	Specific Gravity	Density lb/ft^3
Aluminum	2.70	168.6
Asphalt	1.30	81.2
Basalt	2.75	171.7
Biotite	2.90	181.0
Brick	1.80	112.4
Cement, set	2.85	177.9
Clay, very hard	2.20	137.3
Copper	8.90	555.6
Cork	0.24	15.0
Gold	19.32	1206.1
Gypsum	2.32	144.8
Iron, cast	7.20	449.5
Lead	11.40	711.7
Magnesium	1.74	108.6
Nickel	8.90	555.6
Peat blocks	0.84	52.4
Silver	10.50	655.5
Steel	7.84	489.4
Teflon	2.20	137.3
Zinc	7.19	448.9
Wood		
Alder	0.55	34.3
Birch	0.64	40.0
Cedar	0.53	33.1
Elm	0.57	35.6
Fir	0.51	31.8
Juniper	0.56	35.0
Pine	0.49	30.6
Poplar	0.42	26.2
Spruce	0.59	36.8
Willow	0.50	31.2

8.5   Acceleration Due to Gravity

The acceleration due to gravity, g, at sea level and 45 degrees latitude is:

$9.806\ 160$ m/s^2 or $32.172\ 44$ ft/s^2

8.6   Geographic Constants

One degree of latitude = 69.057 mi
= 111.137 km
One degree of longitude = 48.995 mi
= 78.849 km

8.7   Variation of g (ft/s^2) With Latitude and Elevation

Latitude	Elevation—*ft*					
degrees	0	1000	2000	3000	4000	5000
0	32.0877	32.0847	32.0816	32.0785	32.0754	32.0723
5	32.0890	32.0859	32.0829	32.0798	32.0767	32.0736
10	32.0928	32.0897	32.0867	32.0836	32.0805	32.0774
15	32.0991	32.0960	32.0929	32.0898	32.0867	32.0836
20	32.1075	32.1044	32.1013	32.0983	32.0952	32.0921
25	32.1179	32.1149	32.1118	32.1087	32.1056	32.1025
30	32.1300	32.1269	32.1239	32.1208	32.1177	32.1146
35	32.1434	32.1403	32.1372	32.1341	32.1311	32.1280
40	32.1577	32.1546	32.1515	32.1484	32.1453	32.1422
45	32.1724	32.1693	32.1662	32.1631	32.1601	32.1570
50	32.1871	32.1841	32.1810	32.1779	32.1748	32.1717
55	32.2014	32.1984	32.1953	32.1922	32.1891	32.1860
60	32.2149	32.2118	32.2087	32.2056	32.2025	32.1994
65	32.2270	32.2239	32.2208	32.2178	32.2147	32.2116
70	32.2375	32.2344	32.2313	32.2282	32.2252	32.2221

Latitude	Elevation—*ft*					
degrees	6000	7000	8000	9000	10 000	11 000
0	32.0692	32.0661	32.0631	32.0600	32.0569	32.0538
5	32.0705	32.0674	32.0643	32.0612	32.0582	32.0551
10	32.0743	32.0712	32.0681	32.0651	32.0620	32.0589
15	32.0805	32.0775	32.0744	32.0713	32.0682	32.0651
20	32.0890	32.0859	32.0828	32.0797	32.0767	32.0736
25	32.0994	32.0963	32.0932	32.0902	32.0871	32.0840
30	32.1115	32.1084	32.1053	32.1022	32.0992	32.0961
35	32.1249	32.1218	32.1187	32.1156	32.1125	32.1095
40	32.1392	32.1361	32.1330	32.1299	32.1268	32.1237
45	32.1539	32.1508	32.1477	32.1446	32.1415	32.1385
50	32.1686	32.1655	32.1625	32.1594	32.1563	32.1532
55	32.1829	32.1798	32.1768	32.1737	32.1706	32.1675
60	32.1964	32.1933	32.1902	32.1871	32.1840	32.1809
65	32.2085	32.2054	32.2023	32.1992	32.1962	32.1931
70	32.2190	32.2159	32.2128	32.2097	32.2066	32.2036

8.8   Variation of g (m/s^2) With Latitude and Elevation

Latitude	Elevation—m					
degrees	0	500	1000	1500	2000	2500
0	9.78036	9.77881	9.77727	9.77573	9.77418	9.77264
5	9.78075	9.77920	9.77766	9.77612	9.77458	9.77303
10	9.78191	9.78037	9.77882	9.77728	9.77574	9.77419
15	9.78381	9.78226	9.78072	9.77918	9.77763	9.77609
20	9.78638	9.78484	9.78330	9.78175	9.78021	9.77867
25	9.78956	9.78802	9.78647	9.78493	9.78339	9.78185
30	9.79324	9.79170	9.79016	9.78861	9.78707	9.78553
35	9.79732	9.79578	9.79424	9.79269	9.79115	9.78961
40	9.80167	9.80013	9.79858	9.79704	9.79550	9.79396
45	9.80616	9.80462	9.80307	9.80153	9.79999	9.79845
50	9.81065	9.80911	9.80757	9.80602	9.80448	9.80294
55	9.81501	9.81347	9.81193	9.81038	9.80884	9.80730
60	9.81911	9.81756	9.81602	9.81448	9.81293	9.81139
65	9.82281	9.82126	9.81972	9.81818	9.81664	9.81509
70	9.82601	9.82446	9.82292	9.82138	9.81983	9.81829

Latitude	Elevation—m					
degrees	3000	3500	4000	4500	5000	5500
0	9.77110	9.76956	9.76801	9.76647	9.76493	9.76338
5	9.77149	9.76995	9.76840	9.76686	9.76532	9.76377
10	9.77265	9.77111	9.76956	9.76802	9.76648	9.76494
15	9.77455	9.77301	9.77146	9.76992	9.76838	9.76683
20	9.77712	9.77558	9.77404	9.77250	9.77095	9.76941
25	9.78030	9.77876	9.77722	9.77567	9.77413	9.77259
30	9.78399	9.78244	9.78090	9.77936	9.77781	9.77627
35	9.78806	9.78652	9.78498	9.78343	9.78189	9.78035
40	9.79241	9.79087	9.78933	9.78778	9.78624	9.78470
45	9.79690	9.79536	9.79382	9.79227	9.79073	9.78919
50	9.80139	9.79985	9.79831	9.79677	9.79522	9.79368
55	9.80575	9.80421	9.80267	9.80113	9.79958	9.79804
60	9.80985	9.80830	9.80676	9.80522	9.80368	9.80213
65	9.81355	9.81201	9.81046	9.80892	9.80738	9.80583
70	9.81675	9.81520	9.81366	9.81212	9.81058	9.80903

8.9   Dry Weight of Rocks and Soil

Material	Density	
	lb/ft^3	ton/yd^3
Bentonite, loose	60	0.81
Dolomite	160	2.16
Gneiss	168	2.27
Granite and Porphyry	170	2.30
Greenstone and Trap	187	2.52
Hematite	267	3.60
Limestone	168	2.27
Quartz	165	2.23
Sandstone	151	2.04
Slate	173	2.34
Clay soil, hard	105	1.42
Clay soil, very soft	60	0.81
Silt, compact	115	1.55
Silt, loose	70	0.95
Sand, dense	125	1.69
Sand, loose	75	1.01
Gravel, dense	130	1.76
Gravel, loose	95	1.28
Sandy gravel, dense	140	1.89
Sandy gravel, loose	105	1.42
Clay–silt–sand–gravel, dense	150	2.03
Clay–silt–sand–gravel, loose	100	1.35

9

Hydrometeorological Tables
and Relationships

9.1 Adiabatic Lapse Rates

Unsaturated air = 5.4 °F per 1000 ft
= 9.8 °C per 1000 m

Mean lapse rate = 3.6 °F per 1000 ft
= 6.5 °C per 1000 m

Saturated air = 2.9 °F per 1000 ft
= 5.3 °C per 1000 m

9.2 Standard Atmosphere Chart

Altitude	Temperature		Pressure		Density
ft	°F	°C	lb/in.²	mm Hg	kg/m³
0	59.0	15.0	14.70	760.00	1.2255
1000	55.4	13.0	14.17	732.94	1.1900
2000	51.9	11.0	13.66	706.66	1.1553
3000	48.3	9.1	13.17	681.16	1.1214
4000	44.7	7.1	12.69	656.40	1.0883
5000	41.2	5.1	12.23	632.38	1.0559
6000	37.6	3.1	11.78	609.07	1.0243
7000	34.0	1.1	11.34	586.47	0.9934
8000	30.5	−0.8	10.92	564.55	0.9632
9000	26.9	−2.8	10.51	543.29	0.9337
10 000	23.3	−4.8	10.11	522.69	0.9049
11 000	19.8	−6.8	9.72	502.73	0.8768
12 000	16.2	−8.8	9.35	483.39	0.8494
13 000	12.6	−10.8	8.98	464.65	0.8226
14 000	9.1	−12.7	8.63	446.51	0.7965
15 000	5.5	−14.7	8.29	428.95	0.7710
16 000	1.9	−16.7	7.97	411.95	0.7461
17 000	−1.6	−18.7	7.65	395.50	0.7219
18 000	−5.2	−20.7	7.34	379.58	0.6983
19 000	−8.8	−22.6	7.04	364.19	0.6753
20 000	−12.3	−24.6	6.75	349.31	0.6528
21 000	−15.9	−26.6	6.48	334.92	0.6309
22 000	−19.5	−28.6	6.21	321.02	0.6096
23 000	−23.0	−30.6	5.95	307.59	0.5889
24 000	−26.6	−32.5	5.70	294.61	0.5687
25 000	−30.2	−34.5	5.45	282.09	0.5490
26 000	−33.7	−36.5	5.22	269.99	0.5299
27 000	−37.3	−38.5	5.00	258.33	0.5112
28 000	−40.8	−40.5	4.78	247.07	0.4931
29 000	−44.4	−42.5	4.57	236.21	0.4755
30 000	−48.0	−44.4	4.37	225.75	0.4583

10

Precipitation Gauge Rating Tables

10.1   Time Scale Gears for Belfort Universal Electric Chart Drive

Recording Period		Chart Drive Pinion		Gear in Cylinder	
hours	days	marked	no. teeth	marked	no. teeth
6	0.25	6S	56	6S	49
8	0.33	8S	44	8S	51
12	0.50	12S	40	12S	70
24	1.00	24S	20	24S	70
29	1.21	29S	20	29S	85
48	2.00	48S	52	48S	56
96	4.00	96S	26	96S	56
108	4.50	108S	33	108S	80
144	6.00	144S	23	144S	74
168	7.00	168S	18	168S	68
176	7.33	176S	24	176S	95
192	8.00	192S	20	192S	86
195	8.13	195S	19	195S	83
861	35.88	861S	24	861S	95

10.2   Adjustment Factors for Stick Measurements in 8-in. Orifice Gauges*

Storage Cylinder Diameter in.	Factor	Storage Cylinder Diameter in.	Factor
10.000	1.563	12.750	2.540
10.250	1.642	13.000	2.641
10.500	1.723	13.250	2.743
10.750	1.806	13.500	2.848
11.000	1.891	13.750	2.954
11.250	1.978	14.000	3.063
11.500	2.066	14.250	3.173
11.750	2.157	14.500	3.285
12.000	2.250	14.750	3.399
12.250	2.345	15.000	3.516
12.500	2.441		

*Measurement × factor = precipitation.

10.3   Precipitation Depth–Volume Relationships for Cylindrical Storage Gauges

Volume* units	Orifice Diameter—in.		
	8	10	12
gallons	0.218	0.340	0.490
ounces	27.9	43.5	62.7
millilitres	824	1287	1853

*Volume per inch depth of precipitation.

10.4 Initial Charge of Ethylene Glycol in Seasonal Storage Precipitation Gauges (8-in. Orifice)

Total Precipitation Expected *in.*	Minimum Temperature Expected—°F						
	10	5	0	-5	-10	-15	-20
	Initial Charge of Ethylene Glycol—*quarts*						
10	3	4	4	5	6	6	7
15	4	6	6	8	8	9	10
20	6	7	8	10	11	13	14
25	7	9	10	13	14	16	17
30	9	11	12	15	17	19	21
35	10	13	14	18	19	22	24
40	12	15	16	20	22	25	27
45	13	17	18	23	25	28	31
50	15	19	19	25	28	32	34
55	16	21	21	28	31	35	38
60	17	22	23	30	33	38	41

Total Precipitation Expected *in.*	Minimum Temperature Expected—°F						
	-25	-30	-35	-40	-45	-50	-55
	Initial Charge of Ethylene Glycol—*quarts*						
10	8	8	9	10	10	11	12
15	11	12	13	14	15	17	18
20	15	16	18	19	20	22	24
25	19	20	22	24	26	28	29
30	23	25	26	29	31	33	35
35	26	29	31	34	36	39	41
40	30	33	35	38	41	44	47
45	34	37	40	43	46	50	53
50	38	41	44	48	51	55	59
55	42	45	48	53	56	61	65
60	45	49	53	58	61	66	71

10.5 Dimensions of Sacramento Gauges With 8-in. Orifices

Capacity *in.*	Sidewall Slope	Diameter of Base *in.*	Height *in.*
60	6:1	16.75	26.25
100	6:1	20.31	36.94
200	6:1	24.69	50.06
300	6:1	28.31	60.94
80	8.5:1	16.11	34.47
100	7.2:1	18.00	36.00

10.6   Rating Table for 60-in. Sacramento Storage Gauge*

Stick Depth in.	Equivalent Precipitation—*in.*									
	0.0	0.1	0.2	0.3	0.4	0.5	0.6	0.7	0.8	0.9
0	0.0	0.4	0.9	1.3	1.7	2.2	2.6	3.0	3.5	3.9
1	4.3	4.7	5.1	5.6	6.0	6.4	6.8	7.2	7.6	8.0
2	8.4	8.8	9.2	9.6	10.0	10.4	10.8	11.2	11.6	12.0
3	12.4	12.8	13.2	13.5	13.9	14.3	14.7	15.1	15.4	15.8
4	16.2	16.5	16.9	17.3	17.6	18.0	18.4	18.7	19.1	19.5
5	19.8	20.2	20.5	20.9	21.2	21.6	21.9	22.3	22.6	22.9
6	23.3	23.6	24.0	24.3	24.6	25.0	25.3	25.6	26.0	26.3
7	26.6	26.9	27.3	27.6	27.9	28.2	28.5	28.8	29.2	29.5
8	29.8	30.1	30.4	30.7	31.0	31.3	31.6	31.9	32.2	32.5
9	32.8	33.1	33.4	33.7	34.0	34.3	34.6	34.8	35.1	35.4
10	35.7	36.0	36.3	36.5	36.8	37.1	37.4	37.6	37.9	38.2
11	38.4	38.7	39.0	39.2	39.5	39.8	40.0	40.3	40.5	40.8
12	41.0	41.3	41.5	41.8	42.0	42.3	42.5	42.8	43.0	43.3
13	43.5	43.8	44.0	44.2	44.5	44.7	44.9	45.2	45.4	45.6
14	45.9	46.1	46.3	46.5	46.8	47.0	47.2	47.4	47.6	47.9
15	48.1	48.3	48.5	48.7	48.9	49.1	49.4	49.6	49.8	50.0
16	50.2	50.4	50.6	50.8	51.0	51.2	51.4	51.6	51.8	52.0
17	52.2	52.3	52.5	52.7	52.9	53.1	53.3	53.5	53.7	53.8
18	54.0	54.2	54.4	54.6	54.7	54.9	55.1	55.3	55.4	55.6
19	55.8	55.9	56.1	56.3	56.4	56.6	56.8	56.9	57.1	57.3
20	57.4	57.6	57.7	57.9	58.0	58.2	58.3	58.5	58.6	58.8
21	58.9	59.1	59.2	59.4	59.5	59.7	59.8	60.0	60.1	60.2
22	60.4	60.5	60.7	60.8	60.9	61.1	61.2	61.3	61.5	61.6
23	61.7	61.8	62.0	62.1	62.2	62.4	62.5	62.6	62.7	62.8
24	63.0	63.1	63.2	63.3	63.4	63.5	63.7	63.8	63.9	64.0
25	64.1	64.2	64.3	64.4	64.5	64.7	64.8	64.9	65.0	65.1
26	65.2	65.3	65.4	65.5	65.6	65.7	65.8	65.9	66.0	66.1

*See note below regarding assumptions made in computing this table.

Note: Tables 10.6–10.19 give the theoretical precipitation catch equivalent to the measured depth of liquid in the gauge. The theoretical catch is computed using the formula for the volume of a cone frustrum. Because storage gauges are not always fabricated precisely to the desired dimensions and because gauges may become distorted in operation, calibration of individual gauges is highly recommended if a high degree of accuracy is required.

10.7 Rating Table for 80-in. Sacramento Storage Gauge With 8.5:1 Sidewall Slope*

Stick Depth	Equivalent Precipitation—*in.*									
in.	0.0	0.1	0.2	0.3	0.4	0.5	0.6	0.7	0.8	0.9
0	0.0	0.6	1.1	1.7	2.3	2.8	3.4	4.0	4.5	5.1
1	5.6	6.2	6.7	7.3	7.8	8.4	8.9	9.4	10.0	10.5
2	11.0	11.5	12.1	12.6	13.1	13.6	14.1	14.7	15.2	15.7
3	16.2	16.7	17.2	17.7	18.2	18.7	19.2	19.7	20.2	20.6
4	21.1	21.6	22.1	22.6	23.0	23.5	24.0	24.5	24.9	25.4
5	25.9	26.3	26.8	27.2	27.7	28.1	28.6	29.0	29.5	29.9
6	30.4	30.8	31.2	31.7	32.1	32.5	33.0	33.4	33.8	34.3
7	34.7	35.1	35.5	35.9	36.3	36.8	37.2	37.6	38.0	38.4
8	38.8	39.2	39.6	40.0	40.4	40.8	41.1	41.5	41.9	42.3
9	42.7	43.1	43.4	43.8	44.2	44.6	44.9	45.3	45.7	46.0
10	46.4	46.7	47.1	47.5	47.8	48.2	48.5	48.9	49.2	49.6
11	49.9	50.3	50.6	50.9	51.3	51.6	51.9	52.3	52.6	52.9
12	53.2	53.6	53.9	54.2	54.5	54.8	55.2	55.5	55.8	56.1
13	56.4	56.7	57.0	57.3	57.6	57.9	58.2	58.5	58.8	59.1
14	59.4	59.7	60.0	60.2	60.5	60.8	61.1	61.4	61.7	61.9
15	62.2	62.5	62.7	63.0	63.3	63.5	63.8	64.1	64.3	64.6
16	64.9	65.1	65.4	65.6	65.9	66.1	66.4	66.6	66.9	67.1
17	67.3	67.6	67.8	68.1	68.3	68.5	68.8	69.0	69.2	69.5
18	69.7	69.9	70.1	70.4	70.6	70.8	71.0	71.2	71.4	71.7
19	71.9	72.1	72.3	72.5	72.7	72.9	73.1	73.3	73.5	73.7
20	73.9	74.1	74.3	74.5	74.7	74.9	75.1	75.3	75.5	75.6
21	75.8	76.0	76.2	76.4	76.5	76.7	76.9	77.1	77.3	77.4
22	77.6	77.8	77.9	78.1	78.3	78.4	78.6	78.8	78.9	79.1
23	79.2	79.4	79.6	79.7	79.9	80.0	80.2	80.3	80.5	80.6
24	80.8	80.9	81.0	81.2	81.3	81.5	81.6	81.7	81.9	82.0
25	82.2	82.3	82.4	82.5	82.7	82.8	82.9	83.1	83.2	83.3
26	83.4	83.6	83.7	83.8	83.9	84.0	84.2	84.3	84.4	84.5
27	84.6	84.7	84.8	84.9	85.0	85.2	85.3	85.4	85.5	85.6
28	85.7	85.8	85.9	86.0	86.1	86.2	86.3	86.4	86.5	86.5
29	86.6	86.7	86.8	86.9	87.0	87.1	87.2	87.3	87.3	87.4
30	87.5	87.6	87.7	87.8	87.8	87.9	88.0	88.1	88.1	88.2
31	88.3	88.4	88.4	88.5	88.6	88.7	88.7	88.8	88.9	88.9
32	89.0	89.1	89.1	89.2	89.2	89.3	89.4	89.4	89.5	89.6
33	89.6	89.7	89.7	89.8	89.8	89.9	89.9	90.0	90.0	90.1
34	90.2	90.2	90.3	90.3	90.3	90.4	90.4	90.5	90.5	90.6
35	90.6	90.7	90.7	90.8	90.8	90.8	90.9	90.9	91.0	91.0
36	91.0	91.1	91.1	91.1	91.2	91.2	91.2	91.3	91.3	91.3

*See note on page 64 regarding assumptions made in computing this table.

10.8   Rating Table for 100-in. Sacramento Storage Gauge*

Stick Depth in.	Equivalent Precipitation—*in.*									
	0.0	0.1	0.2	0.3	0.4	0.5	0.6	0.7	0.8	0.9
0	0.0	0.6	1.3	1.9	2.6	3.2	3.8	4.5	5.1	5.7
1	6.3	7.0	7.6	8.2	8.8	9.4	10.0	10.7	11.3	11.9
2	12.5	13.1	13.7	14.3	14.9	15.5	16.1	16.6	17.2	17.8
3	18.4	19.0	19.6	20.1	20.7	21.3	21.9	22.4	23.0	23.6
4	24.1	24.7	25.3	25.8	26.4	26.9	27.5	28.0	28.6	29.1
5	29.7	30.2	30.7	31.3	31.8	32.4	32.9	33.4	33.9	34.5
6	35.0	35.5	36.0	36.6	37.1	37.6	38.1	38.6	39.1	39.6
7	40.1	40.6	41.1	41.6	42.1	42.6	43.1	43.6	44.1	44.6
8	45.1	45.6	46.1	46.5	47.0	47.5	48.0	48.5	48.9	49.4
9	49.9	50.3	50.8	51.3	51.7	52.2	52.6	53.1	53.6	54.0
10	54.5	54.9	55.4	55.8	56.3	56.7	57.1	57.6	58.0	58.4
11	58.9	59.3	59.7	60.2	60.6	61.0	61.4	61.9	62.3	62.7
12	63.1	63.5	64.0	64.4	64.8	65.2	65.6	66.0	66.4	66.8
13	67.2	67.6	68.0	68.4	68.8	69.2	69.6	69.9	70.3	70.7
14	71.1	71.5	71.9	72.2	72.6	73.0	73.4	73.7	74.1	74.5
15	74.8	75.2	75.6	75.9	76.3	76.7	77.0	77.4	77.7	78.1
16	78.4	78.8	79.1	79.5	79.8	80.2	80.5	80.8	81.2	81.5
17	81.9	82.2	82.5	82.9	83.2	83.5	83.8	84.2	84.5	84.8
18	85.1	85.5	85.8	86.1	86.4	86.7	87.0	87.3	87.6	88.0
19	88.3	88.6	88.9	89.2	89.5	89.8	90.1	90.4	90.7	91.0
20	91.2	91.5	91.8	92.1	92.4	92.7	93.0	93.2	93.5	93.8
21	94.1	94.4	94.6	94.9	95.2	95.4	95.7	96.0	96.3	96.5
22	96.8	97.0	97.3	97.6	97.8	98.1	98.3	98.6	98.8	99.1
23	99.3	99.6	99.8	100.1	100.3	100.6	100.8	101.1	101.3	101.5
24	101.8	102.0	102.3	102.5	102.7	102.9	103.2	103.4	103.6	103.9
25	104.1	104.3	104.5	104.8	105.0	105.2	105.4	105.6	105.8	106.1
26	106.3	106.5	106.7	106.9	107.1	107.3	107.5	107.7	107.9	108.1
27	108.3	108.5	108.7	108.9	109.1	109.3	109.5	109.7	109.9	110.1
28	110.3	110.5	110.6	110.8	111.0	111.2	111.4	111.6	111.7	111.9
29	112.1	112.3	112.4	112.6	112.8	113.0	113.1	113.3	113.5	113.6
30	113.8	114.0	114.1	114.3	114.5	114.6	114.8	114.9	115.1	115.3
31	115.4	115.6	115.7	115.9	116.0	116.2	116.3	116.5	116.6	116.8
32	116.9	117.1	117.2	117.4	117.5	117.6	117.8	117.9	118.1	118.2
33	118.3	118.5	118.6	118.7	118.9	119.0	119.1	119.2	119.4	119.5
34	119.6	119.8	119.9	120.0	120.1	120.3	120.4	120.5	120.6	120.7
35	120.8	121.0	121.1	121.2	121.3	121.4	121.5	121.6	121.8	121.9
36	122.0	122.1	122.2	122.3	122.4	122.5	122.6	122.7	122.8	122.9

*See note on page 64 regarding assumptions made in computing this table.

10.9 Rating Table for 100-in. Sacramento Storage Gauge With 7.2:1 Sidewall Slope*

Stick Depth	Equivalent Precipitation—*in.*									
in.	0.0	0.1	0.2	0.3	0.4	0.5	0.6	0.7	0.8	0.9
0	0.0	0.6	1.2	1.8	2.4	3.0	3.6	4.2	4.8	5.4
1	6.0	6.5	7.1	7.7	8.3	8.9	9.4	10.0	10.6	11.1
2	11.7	12.3	12.8	13.4	13.9	14.5	15.0	15.6	16.1	16.7
3	17.2	17.8	18.3	18.8	19.4	19.9	20.4	21.0	21.5	22.0
4	22.5	23.1	23.6	24.1	24.6	25.1	25.6	26.1	26.6	27.1
5	27.6	28.1	28.6	29.1	29.6	30.1	30.6	31.1	31.6	32.1
6	32.5	33.0	33.5	34.0	34.5	34.9	35.4	35.9	36.3	36.8
7	37.2	37.7	38.2	38.6	39.1	39.5	40.0	40.4	40.9	41.3
8	41.8	42.2	42.6	43.1	43.5	43.9	44.4	44.8	45.2	45.6
9	46.1	46.5	46.9	47.3	47.7	48.2	48.6	49.0	49.4	49.8
10	50.2	50.6	51.0	51.4	51.8	52.2	52.6	53.0	53.4	53.7
11	54.1	54.5	54.9	55.3	55.7	56.0	56.4	56.8	57.2	57.5
12	57.9	58.3	58.6	59.0	59.4	59.7	60.1	60.4	60.8	61.1
13	61.5	61.8	62.2	62.5	62.9	63.2	63.6	63.9	64.2	64.6
14	64.9	65.2	65.6	65.9	66.2	66.5	66.9	67.2	67.5	67.8
15	68.2	68.5	68.8	69.1	69.4	69.7	70.0	70.3	70.6	70.9
16	71.2	71.5	71.8	72.1	72.4	72.7	73.0	73.3	73.6	73.9
17	74.2	74.5	74.7	75.0	75.3	75.6	75.9	76.1	76.4	76.7
18	76.9	77.2	77.5	77.7	78.0	78.3	78.5	78.8	79.1	79.3
19	79.6	79.8	80.1	80.3	80.6	80.8	81.1	81.3	81.6	81.8
20	82.0	82.3	82.5	82.8	83.0	83.2	83.5	83.7	83.9	84.2
21	84.4	84.6	84.8	85.1	85.3	85.5	85.7	85.9	86.2	86.4
22	86.6	86.8	87.0	87.2	87.4	87.6	87.8	88.0	88.3	88.5
23	88.7	88.9	89.1	89.2	89.4	89.6	89.8	90.0	90.2	90.4
24	90.6	90.8	91.0	91.1	91.3	91.5	91.7	91.9	92.1	92.2
25	92.4	92.6	92.8	92.9	93.1	93.3	93.4	93.6	93.8	93.9
26	94.1	94.3	94.4	94.6	94.7	94.9	95.1	95.2	95.4	95.5
27	95.7	95.8	96.0	96.1	96.3	96.4	96.6	96.7	96.9	97.0
28	97.1	97.3	97.4	97.6	97.7	97.8	98.0	98.1	98.2	98.4
29	98.5	98.6	98.7	98.9	99.0	99.1	99.3	99.4	99.5	99.6
30	99.7	99.9	100.0	100.1	100.2	100.3	100.4	100.6	100.7	100.8
31	100.9	101.0	101.1	101.2	101.3	101.4	101.5	101.6	101.7	101.8
32	101.9	102.0	102.1	102.2	102.3	102.4	102.5	102.6	102.7	102.8
33	102.9	103.0	103.1	103.2	103.3	103.4	103.4	103.5	103.6	103.7
34	103.8	103.9	103.9	104.0	104.1	104.2	104.3	104.3	104.4	104.5
35	104.6	104.7	104.7	104.8	104.9	104.9	105.0	105.1	105.2	105.2
36	105.3	105.4	105.4	105.5	105.6	105.6	105.7	105.7	105.8	105.9

*See note on page 64 regarding assumptions made in computing this table.

10.10   Rating Table for 200-in. Sacramento Storage Gauge*

Stick Depth in.	Equivalent Precipitation—*in.*									
	0.0	0.1	0.2	0.3	0.4	0.5	0.6	0.7	0.8	0.9
0	0.0	1.0	1.9	2.8	3.8	4.7	5.7	6.6	7.5	8.5
1	9.4	10.3	11.2	12.2	13.1	14.0	14.9	15.8	16.7	17.6
2	18.5	19.4	20.3	21.2	22.1	23.0	23.9	24.8	25.7	26.6
3	27.4	28.3	29.2	30.0	30.9	31.8	32.6	33.5	34.4	35.2
4	36.1	36.9	37.8	38.6	39.5	40.3	41.1	42.0	42.8	43.6
5	44.5	45.3	46.1	46.9	47.8	48.6	49.4	50.2	51.0	51.8
6	52.6	53.4	54.2	55.0	55.8	56.6	57.4	58.2	59.0	59.8
7	60.6	61.3	62.1	62.9	63.7	64.4	65.2	66.0	66.7	67.5
8	68.3	69.0	69.8	70.5	71.3	72.0	72.8	73.5	74.2	75.0
9	75.7	76.5	77.2	77.9	78.6	79.4	80.1	80.8	81.5	82.2
10	83.0	83.7	84.4	85.1	85.8	86.5	87.2	87.9	88.6	89.3
11	90.0	90.7	91.3	92.0	92.7	93.4	94.1	94.7	95.4	96.1
12	96.8	97.4	98.1	98.8	99.4	100.1	100.7	101.4	102.0	102.7
13	103.3	104.0	104.6	105.3	105.9	106.6	107.2	107.8	108.5	109.1
14	109.7	110.3	111.0	111.6	112.2	112.8	113.4	114.0	114.7	115.3
15	115.9	116.5	117.1	117.7	118.3	118.9	119.5	120.1	120.7	121.2
16	121.8	122.4	123.0	123.6	124.2	124.7	125.3	125.9	126.4	127.0
17	127.6	128.1	128.7	129.3	129.8	130.4	130.9	131.5	132.0	132.6
18	133.1	133.7	134.2	134.8	135.3	135.8	136.4	136.9	137.4	138.0
19	138.5	139.0	139.5	140.1	140.6	141.1	141.6	142.1	142.6	143.2
20	143.7	144.2	144.7	145.2	145.7	146.2	146.7	147.2	147.7	148.2
21	148.6	149.1	149.6	150.1	150.6	151.1	151.5	152.0	152.5	153.0
22	153.4	153.9	154.4	154.8	155.3	155.8	156.2	156.7	157.1	157.6
23	158.1	158.5	159.0	159.4	159.9	160.3	160.7	161.2	161.6	162.1
24	162.5	162.9	163.4	163.8	164.2	164.7	165.1	165.5	165.9	166.3
25	166.8	167.2	167.6	168.0	168.4	168.8	169.2	169.6	170.1	170.5
26	170.9	171.3	171.7	172.1	172.4	172.8	173.2	173.6	174.0	174.4
27	174.8	175.2	175.6	175.9	176.3	176.7	177.1	177.4	177.8	178.2
28	178.5	178.9	179.3	179.6	180.0	180.4	180.7	181.1	181.4	181.8
29	182.2	182.5	182.9	183.2	183.6	183.9	184.2	184.6	184.9	185.3
30	185.6	185.9	186.3	186.6	186.9	187.3	187.6	187.9	188.2	188.6
31	188.9	189.2	189.5	189.9	190.2	190.5	190.8	191.1	191.4	191.7
32	192.0	192.3	192.7	193.0	193.3	193.6	193.9	194.2	194.5	194.7
33	195.0	195.3	195.6	195.9	196.2	196.5	196.8	197.1	197.3	197.6
34	197.9	198.2	198.5	198.7	199.0	199.3	199.5	199.8	200.1	200.4
35	200.6	200.9	201.1	201.4	201.7	201.9	202.2	202.4	202.7	202.9
36	203.2	203.4	203.7	203.9	204.2	204.4	204.7	204.9	205.2	205.4
37	205.6	205.9	206.1	206.4	206.6	206.8	207.1	207.3	207.5	207.7
38	208.0	208.2	208.4	208.6	208.9	209.1	209.3	209.5	209.7	210.0
39	210.2	210.4	210.6	210.8	211.0	211.2	211.4	211.6	211.8	212.0
40	212.2	212.4	212.6	212.8	213.0	213.2	213.4	213.6	213.8	214.0
41	214.2	214.4	214.6	214.8	214.9	215.1	215.3	215.5	215.7	215.9
42	216.0	216.2	216.4	216.6	216.7	216.9	217.1	217.3	217.4	217.6
43	217.8	217.9	218.1	218.3	218.4	218.6	218.8	218.9	219.1	219.2
44	219.4	219.5	219.7	219.9	220.0	220.2	220.3	220.5	220.6	220.8
45	220.9	221.1	221.2	221.3	221.5	221.6	221.8	221.9	222.0	222.2
46	222.3	222.5	222.6	222.7	222.9	223.0	223.1	223.3	223.4	223.5
47	223.6	223.8	223.9	224.0	224.1	224.3	224.4	224.5	224.6	224.7
48	224.9	225.0	225.1	225.2	225.3	225.4	225.6	225.7	225.8	225.9

*See note on page 64 regarding assumptions made in computing this table.

10.11   Rating Table for 200-in. Sacramento Storage Gauge With 10-in. Orifice Conversion*

Stick Depth *in.*	Equivalent Precipitation—*in.*									
	0.0	0.1	0.2	0.3	0.4	0.5	0.6	0.7	0.8	0.9
0	0.0	0.6	1.2	1.8	2.4	3.0	3.6	4.2	4.8	5.4
1	6.0	6.6	7.2	7.8	8.4	9.0	9.5	10.1	10.7	11.3
2	11.9	12.4	13.0	13.6	14.2	14.7	15.3	15.9	16.4	17.0
3	17.6	18.1	18.7	19.2	19.8	20.3	20.9	21.4	22.0	22.5
4	23.1	23.6	24.2	24.7	25.3	25.8	26.3	26.9	27.4	27.9
5	28.5	29.0	29.5	30.0	30.6	31.1	31.6	32.1	32.7	33.2
6	33.7	34.2	34.7	35.2	35.7	36.2	36.7	37.3	37.8	38.3
7	38.8	39.3	39.8	40.3	40.7	41.2	41.7	42.2	42.7	43.2
8	43.7	44.2	44.6	45.1	45.6	46.1	46.6	47.0	47.5	48.0
9	48.5	48.9	49.4	49.9	50.3	50.8	51.3	51.7	52.2	52.6
10	53.1	53.5	54.0	54.5	54.9	55.4	55.8	56.2	56.7	57.1
11	57.6	58.0	58.5	58.9	59.3	59.8	60.2	60.6	61.1	61.5
12	61.9	62.4	62.8	63.2	63.6	64.1	64.5	64.9	65.3	65.7
13	66.1	66.6	67.0	67.4	67.8	68.2	68.6	69.0	69.4	69.8
14	70.2	70.6	71.0	71.4	71.8	72.2	72.6	73.0	73.4	73.8
15	74.2	74.5	74.9	75.3	75.7	76.1	76.5	76.8	77.2	77.6
16	78.0	78.3	78.7	79.1	79.5	79.8	80.2	80.6	80.9	81.3
17	81.7	82.0	82.4	82.7	83.1	83.4	83.8	84.2	84.5	84.9
18	85.2	85.6	85.9	86.2	86.6	86.9	87.3	87.6	88.0	88.3
19	88.6	89.0	89.3	89.6	90.0	90.3	90.6	91.0	91.3	91.6
20	91.9	92.3	92.6	92.9	93.2	93.6	93.9	94.2	94.5	94.8
21	95.1	95.4	95.8	96.1	96.4	96.7	97.0	97.3	97.6	97.9
22	98.2	98.5	98.8	99.1	99.4	99.7	100.0	100.3	100.6	100.9
23	101.2	101.4	101.7	102.0	102.3	102.6	102.9	103.2	103.4	103.7
24	104.0	104.3	104.6	104.8	105.1	105.4	105.6	105.9	106.2	106.5
25	106.7	107.0	107.3 .	107.5	107.8	108.1	108.3	108.6	108.8	109.1
26	109.3	109.6	109.9	110.1	110.4	110.6	110.9	111.1	111.4	111.6
27	111.9	112.1	112.4	112.6	112.8	113.1	113.3	113.6	113.8	114.0
28	114.3	114.5	114.7	115.0	115.2	115.4	115.7	115.9	116.1	116.4
29	116.6	116.8	117.0	117.3	117.5	117.7	117.9	118.1	118.4	118.6
30	118.8	119.0	119.2	119.4	119.6	119.9	120.1	120.3	120.5	120.7
31	120.9	121.1	121.3	121.5	121.7	121.9	122.1	122.3	122.5	122.7
32	122.9	123.1	123.3	123.5	123.7	123.9	124.1	124.3	124.5	124.6
33	124.8	125.0	125.2	125.4	125.6	125.8	125.9	126.1	126.3	126.5
34	126.7	126.8	127.0	127.2	127.4	127.5	127.7	127.9	128.1	128.2
35	128.4	128.6	128.7	128.9	129.1	129.2	129.4	129.6	129.7	129.9
36	130.0	130.2	130.4	130.5	130.7	130.8	131.0	131.2	131.3	131.5
37	131.6	131.8	131.9	132.1	132.2	132.4	132.5	132.7	132.8	133.0
38	133.1	133.2	133.4	133.5	133.7	133.8	134.0	134.1	134.2	134.4
39	134.5	134.6	134.8	134.9	135.0	135.2	135.3	135.4	135.6	135.7
40	135.8	136.0	136.1	136.2	136.3	136.5	136.6	136.7	136.8	137.0
41	137.1	137.2	137.3	137.4	137.6	137.7	137.8	137.9	138.0	138.1
42	138.3	138.4	138.5	138.6	138.7	138.8	138.9	139.0	139.2	139.3
43	139.4	139.5	139.6	139.7	139.8	139.9	140.0	140.1	140.2	140.3
44	140.4	140.5	140.6	140.7	140.8	140.9	141.0	141.1	141.2	141.3
45	141.4	141.5	141.6	141.7	141.8	141.8	141.9	142.0	142.1	142.2
46	142.3	142.4	142.5	142.5	142.6	142.7	142.8	142.9	143.0	143.0
47	143.1	143.2	143.3	143.4	143.5	143.5	143.6	143.7	143.8	143.8
48	143.9	144.0	144.1	144.1	144.2	144.3	144.4	144.4	144.5	144.6

*See note on page 64 regarding assumptions made in computing this table.

10.12   Rating Table for 200-in. Sacramento Storage Gauge With 12-in. Orifice Conversion*

Stick Depth	Equivalent Precipitation—*in.*									
in.	0.0	0.1	0.2	0.3	0.4	0.5	0.6	0.7	0.8	0.9
0	0.0	0.4	0.8	1.3	1.7	2.1	2.5	2.9	3.3	3.8
1	4.2	4.6	5.0	5.4	5.8	6.2	6.6	7.0	7.4	7.8
2	8.2	8.6	9.0	9.4	9.8	10.2	10.6	11.0	11.4	11.8
3	12.2	12.6	13.0	13.4	13.7	14.1	14.5	14.9	15.3	15.7
4	16.0	16.4	16.8	17.2	17.5	17.9	18.3	18.7	19.0	19.4
5	19.8	20.1	20.5	20.9	21.2	21.6	22.0	22.3	22.7	23.0
6	23.4	23.7	24.1	24.5	24.8	25.2	25.5	25.9	26.2	26.6
7	26.9	27.3	27.6	27.9	28.3	28.6	29.0	29.3	29.7	30.0
8	30.3	30.7	31.0	31.3	31.7	32.0	32.3	32.7	33.0	33.3
9	33.6	34.0	34.3	34.6	34.9	35.3	35.6	35.9	36.2	36.5
10	36.9	37.2	37.5	37.8	38.1	38.4	38.7	39.1	39.4	39.7
11	40.0	40.3	40.6	40.9	41.2	41.5	41.8	42.1	42.4	42.7
12	43.0	43.3	43.6	43.9	44.2	44.5	44.8	45.1	45.3	45.6
13	45.9	46.2	46.5	46.8	47.1	47.4	47.6	47.9	48.2	48.5
14	48.8	49.0	49.3	49.6	49.9	50.1	50.4	50.7	51.0	51.2
15	51.5	51.8	52.0	52.3	52.6	52.8	53.1	53.4	53.6	53.9
16	54.1	54.4	54.7	54.9	55.2	55.4	55.7	55.9	56.2	56.4
17	56.7	56.9	57.2	57.4	57.7	57.9	58.2	58.4	58.7	58.9
18	59.2	59.4	59.6	59.9	60.1	60.4	60.6	60.8	61.1	61.3
19	61.5	61.8	62.0	62.2	62.5	62.7	62.9	63.2	63.4	63.6
20	63.8	64.1	64.3	64.5	64.7	65.0	65.2	65.4	65.6	65.8
21	66.1	66.3	66.5	66.7	66.9	67.1	67.3	67.6	67.8	68.0
22	68.2	68.4	68.6	68.8	69.0	69.2	69.4	69.6	69.8	70.0
23	70.2	70.4	70.6	70.8	71.0	71.2	71.4	71.6	71.8	72.0
24	72.2	72.4	72.6	72.8	73.0	73.2	73.4	73.5	73.7	73.9
25	74.1	74.3	74.5	74.7	74.8	75.0	75.2	75.4	75.6	75.8
26	75.9	76.1	76.3	76.5	76.6	76.8	77.0	77.2	77.3	77.5
27	77.7	77.8	78.0	78.2	78.4	78.5	78.7	78.9	79.0	79.2
28	79.3	79.5	79.7	79.8	80.0	80.2	80.3	80.5	80.6	80.8
29	80.9	81.1	81.3	81.4	81.6	81.7	81.9	82.0	82.2	82.3
30	82.5	82.6	82.8	82.9	83.1	83.2	83.4	83.5	83.7	83.8
31	83.9	84.1	84.2	84.4	84.5	84.7	84.8	84.9	85.1	85.2
32	85.3	85.5	85.6	85.8	85.9	86.0	86.2	86.3	86.4	86.5
33	86.7	86.8	86.9	87.1	87.2	87.3	87.4	87.6	87.7	87.8
34	87.9	88.1	88.2	88.3	88.4	88.6	88.7	88.8	88.9	89.0
35	89.2	89.3	89.4	89.5	89.6	89.7	89.8	90.0	90.1	90.2
36	90.3	90.4	90.5	90.6	90.7	90.9	91.0	91.1	91.2	91.3
37	91.4	91.5	91.6	91.7	91.8	91.9	92.0	92.1	92.2	92.3
38	92.4	92.5	92.6	92.7	92.8	92.9	93.0	93.1	93.2	93.3
39	93.4	93.5	93.6	93.7	93.8	93.9	94.0	94.0	94.1	94.2
40	94.3	94.4	94.5	94.6	94.7	94.8	94.8	94.9	95.0	95.1
41	95.2	95.3	95.4	95.4	95.5	95.6	95.7	95.8	95.8	95.9
42	96.0	96.1	96.2	96.2	96.3	96.4	96.5	96.5	96.6	96.7
43	96.8	96.8	96.9	97.0	97.1	97.1	97.2	97.3	97.4	97.4
44	97.5	97.6	97.6	97.7	97.8	97.8	97.9	98.0	98.0	98.1
45	98.2	98.2	98.3	98.4	98.4	98.5	98.6	98.6	98.7	98.7
46	98.8	98.9	98.9	99.0	99.0	99.1	99.2	99.2	99.3	99.3
47	99.4	99.4	99.5	99.6	99.6	99.7	99.7	99.8	99.8	99.9
48	99.9	100.0	100.0	100.1	100.1	100.2	100.2	100.3	100.3	100.4

*See note on page 64 regarding assumptions made in computing this table.

10.13   Rating Table for 300-in. Sacramento Storage Gauge*

Stick Depth in.	Equivalent Precipitation—*in.*									
	0.0	0.1	0.2	0.3	0.4	0.5	0.6	0.7	0.8	0.9
0	0.0	1.3	2.5	3.7	5.0	6.2	7.5	8.7	9.9	11.2
1	12.4	13.6	14.8	16.0	17.2	18.5	19.7	20.9	22.1	23.3
2	24.5	25.7	26.8	28.0	29.2	30.4	31.6	32.8	33.9	35.1
3	36.3	37.4	38.6	39.7	40.9	42.1	43.2	44.4	45.5	46.6
4	47.8	48.9	50.0	51.2	52.3	53.4	54.5	55.7	56.8	57.9
5	59.0	60.1	61.2	62.3	63.4	64.5	65.6	66.7	67.8	68.9
6	70.0	71.0	72.1	73.2	74.3	75.3	76.4	77.5	78.5	79.6
7	80.6	81.7	82.7	83.8	84.8	85.9	86.9	88.0	89.0	90.0
8	91.1	92.1	93.1	94.1	95.1	96.2	97.2	98.2	99.2	100.2
9	101.2	102.2	103.2	104.2	105.2	106.2	107.2	108.1	109.1	110.1
10	111.1	112.1	113.0	114.0	115.0	115.9	116.9	117.8	118.8	119.7
11	120.7	121.6	122.6	123.5	124.5	125.4	126.3	127.3	128.2	129.1
12	130.1	131.0	131.9	132.8	133.7	134.6	135.6	136.5	137.4	138.3
13	139.2	140.1	141.0	141.9	142.7	143.6	144.5	145.4	146.3	147.2
14	148.0	148.9	149.8	150.6	151.5	152.4	153.2	154.1	154.9	155.8
15	156.6	157.5	158.3	159.2	160.0	160.9	161.7	162.5	163.4	164.2
16	165.0	165.8	166.7	167.5	168.3	169.1	169.9	170.7	171.5	172.3
17	173.1	173.9	174.7	175.5	176.3	177.1	177.9	178.7	179.5	180.3
18	181.0	181.8	182.6	183.4	184.1	184.9	185.7	186.4	187.2	187.9
19	188.7	189.5	190.2	191.0	191.7	192.4	193.2	193.9	194.7	195.4
20	196.1	196.9	197.6	198.3	199.0	199.8	200.5	201.2	201.9	202.6
21	203.3	204.1	204.8	205.5	206.2	206.9	207.6	208.3	209.0	209.6
22	210.3	211.0	211.7	212.4	213.1	213.7	214.4	215.1	215.8	216.4
23	217.1	217.8	218.4	219.1	219.7	220.4	221.1	221.7	222.4	223.0
24	223.7	224.3	224.9	225.6	226.2	226.8	227.5	228.1	228.7	229.4
25	230.0	230.6	231.2	231.9	232.5	233.1	233.7	234.3	234.9	235.5
26	236.1	236.7	237.3	237.9	238.5	239.1	239.7	240.3	240.9	241.5
27	242.1	242.6	243.2	243.8	244.4	244.9	245.5	246.1	246.7	247.2
28	247.8	248.3	248.9	249.5	250.0	250.6	251.1	251.7	252.2	252.8
29	253.3	253.9	254.4	254.9	255.5	256.0	256.5	257.1	257.6	258.1
30	258.6	259.2	259.7	260.2	260.7	261.2	261.8	262.3	262.8	263.3
31	263.8	264.3	264.8	265.3	265.8	266.3	266.8	267.3	267.8	268.3
32	268.8	269.2	269.7	270.2	270.7	271.2	271.6	272.1	272.6	273.1
33	273.5	274.0	274.5	274.9	275.4	275.8	276.3	276.8	277.2	277.7
34	278.1	278.6	279.0	279.5	279.9	280.3	280.8	281.2	281.7	282.1
35	282.5	283.0	283.4	283.8	284.3	284.7	285.1	285.5	285.9	286.4
36	286.8	287.2	287.6	288.0	288.4	288.8	289.2	289.6	290.0	290.5
37	290.8	291.2	291.6	292.0	292.4	292.8	293.2	293.6	294.0	294.4
38	294.8	295.1	295.5	295.9	296.3	296.6	297.0	297.4	297.8	298.1
39	298.5	298.9	299.2	299.6	300.0	300.3	300.7	301.0	301.4	301.7
40	302.1	302.4	302.8	303.1	303.5	303.8	304.2	304.5	304.8	305.2
41	305.5	305.8	306.2	306.5	306.8	307.2	307.5	307.8	308.1	308.5
42	308.8	309.1	309.4	309.7	310.1	310.4	310.7	311.0	311.3	311.6
43	311.9	312.2	312.5	312.8	313.1	313.4	313.7	314.0	314.3	314.6
44	314.9	315.2	315.5	315.8	316.0	316.3	316.6	316.9	317.2	317.5
45	317.7	318.0	318.3	318.6	318.8	319.1	319.4	319.6	319.9	320.2
46	320.4	320.7	321.0	321.2	321.5	321.7	322.0	322.2	322.5	322.7
47	323.0	323.2	323.5	323.7	324.0	324.2	324.5	324.7	325.0	325.2
48	325.4	325.7	325.9	326.1	326.4	326.6	326.8	327.1	327.3	327.5

*See note on page 64 regarding assumptions made in computing this table.

10.14 Rating Table for 300-in. Sacramento Storage Gauge With 10-in. Orifice Conversion*

Stick Depth	Equivalent Precipitation—*in.*									
in.	0.0	0.1	0.2	0.3	0.4	0.5	0.6	0.7	0.8	0.9
0	0.0	0.8	1.6	2.4	3.2	4.0	4.8	5.6	6.4	7.1
1	7.9	8.7	9.5	10.3	11.0	11.8	12.6	13.4	14.1	14.9
2	15.7	16.4	17.2	17.9	18.7	19.5	20.2	21.0	21.7	22.5
3	23.2	24.0	24.7	25.4	26.2	26.9	27.7	28.4	29.1	29.8
4	30.6	31.3	32.0	32.8	33.5	34.2	34.9	35.6	36.3	37.1
5	37.8	38.5	39.2	39.9	40.6	41.3	42.0	42.7	43.4	44.1
6	44.8	45.5	46.2	46.8	47.5	48.2	48.9	49.6	50.3	50.9
7	51.6	52.3	53.0	53.6	54.3	55.0	55.6	56.3	57.0	57.6
8	58.3	58.9	59.6	60.2	60.9	61.5	62.2	62.8	63.5	64.1
9	64.8	65.4	66.0	66.7	67.3	67.9	68.6	69.2	69.8	70.5
10	71.1	71.7	72.3	73.0	73.6	74.2	74.8	75.4	76.0	76.6
11	77.2	77.9	78.5	79.1	79.7	80.3	80.9	81.5	82.1	82.6
12	83.2	83.8	84.4	85.0	85.6	86.2	86.8	87.3	87.9	88.5
13	89.1	89.6	90.2	90.8	91.4	91.9	92.5	93.1	93.6	94.2
14	94.7	95.3	95.9	96.4	97.0	97.5	98.1	98.6	99.2	99.7
15	100.3	100.8	101.3	101.9	102.4	102.9	103.5	104.0	104.5	105.1
16	105.6	106.1	106.7	107.2	107.7	108.2	108.7	109.3	109.8	110.3
17	110.8	111.3	111.8	112.3	112.9	113.4	113.9	114.4	114.9	115.4
18	115.9	116.4	116.9	117.4	117.8	118.3	118.8	119.3	119.8	120.3
19	120.8	121.3	121.7	122.2	122.7	123.2	123.6	124.1	124.6	125.1
20	125.5	126.0	126.5	126.9	127.4	127.9	128.3	128.8	129.2	129.7
21	130.1	130.6	131.0	131.5	131.9	132.4	132.8	133.3	133.7	134.2
22	134.6	135.1	135.5	135.9	136.4	136.8	137.2	137.7	138.1	138.5
23	138.9	139.4	139.8	140.2	140.6	141.1	141.5	141.9	142.3	142.7
24	143.1	143.5	144.0	144.4	144.8	145.2	145.6	146.0	146.4	146.8
25	147.2	147.6	148.0	148.4	148.8	149.2	149.6	150.0	150.3	150.7
26	151.1	151.5	151.9	152.3	152.7	153.0	153.4	153.8	154.2	154.5
27	154.9	155.3	155.7	156.0	156.4	156.8	157.1	157.5	157.9	158.2
28	158.6	158.9	159.3	159.7	160.0	160.4	160.7	161.1	161.4	161.8
29	162.1	162.5	162.8	163.2	163.5	163.8	164.2	164.5	164.9	165.2
30	165.5	165.9	166.2	166.5	166.9	167.2	167.5	167.9	168.2	168.5
31	168.8	169.2	169.5	169.8	170.1	170.4	170.7	171.1	171.4	171.7
32	172.0	172.3	172.6	172.9	173.2	173.5	173.8	174.2	174.5	174.8
33	175.1	175.4	175.7	175.9	176.2	176.5	176.8	177.1	177.4	177.7
34	178.0	178.3	178.6	178.9	179.1	179.4	179.7	180.0	180.3	180.5
35	180.8	181.1	181.4	181.6	181.9	182.2	182.5	182.7	183.0	183.3
36	183.5	183.8	184.1	184.3	184.6	184.9	185.1	185.4	185.6	185.9
37	186.1	186.4	186.7	186.9	187.2	187.4	187.7	187.9	188.2	188.4
38	188.6	188.9	189.1	189.4	189.6	189.9	190.1	190.3	190.6	190.8
39	191.0	191.3	191.5	191.7	192.0	192.2	192.4	192.7	192.9	193.1
40	193.3	193.6	193.8	194.0	194.2	194.4	194.7	194.9	195.1	195.3
41	195.5	195.7	196.0	196.2	196.4	196.6	196.8	197.0	197.2	197.4
42	197.6	197.8	198.0	198.2	198.4	198.6	198.8	199.0	199.2	199.4
43	199.6	199.8	200.0	200.2	200.4	200.6	200.8	201.0	201.2	201.3
44	201.5	201.7	201.9	202.1	202.3	202.5	202.6	202.8	203.0	203.2
45	203.4	203.5	203.7	203.9	204.1	204.2	204.4	204.6	204.7	204.9
46	205.1	205.2	205.4	205.6	205.7	205.9	206.1	206.2	206.4	206.6
47	206.7	206.9	207.0	207.2	207.4	207.5	207.7	207.8	208.0	208.1
48	208.3	208.4	208.6	208.7	208.9	209.0	209.2	209.3	209.5	209.6

*See note on page 64 regarding assumptions made in computing this table.

10.15 Rating Table for 300-in. Sacramento Storage Gauge With 12-in. Orifice Conversion*

Stick Depth in.	Equivalent Precipitation—in.									
	0.0	0.1	0.2	0.3	0.4	0.5	0.6	0.7	0.8	0.9
0	0.0	0.6	1.1	1.7	2.2	2.8	3.3	3.9	4.4	5.0
1	5.5	6.0	6.6	7.1	7.7	8.2	8.7	9.3	9.8	10.3
2	10.9	11.4	11.9	12.5	13.0	13.5	14.0	14.6	15.1	15.6
3	16.1	16.6	17.1	17.7	18.2	18.7	19.2	19.7	20.2	20.7
4	21.2	21.7	22.2	22.7	23.2	23.7	24.2	24.7	25.2	25.7
5	26.2	26.7	27.2	27.7	28.2	28.7	29.2	29.6	30.1	30.6
6	31.1	31.6	32.1	32.5	33.0	33.5	34.0	34.4	34.9	35.4
7	35.8	36.3	36.8	37.2	37.7	38.2	38.6	39.1	39.5	40.0
8	40.5	40.9	41.4	41.8	42.3	42.7	43.2	43.6	44.1	44.5
9	45.0	45.4	45.9	46.3	46.7	47.2	47.6	48.1	48.5	48.9
10	49.4	49.8	50.2	50.7	51.1	51.5	51.9	52.4	52.8	53.2
11	53.6	54.1	54.5	54.9	55.3	55.7	56.1	56.6	57.0	57.4
12	57.8	58.2	58.6	59.0	59.4	59.8	60.2	60.6	61.0	61.4
13	61.8	62.2	62.6	63.0	63.4	63.8	64.2	64.6	65.0	65.4
14	65.8	66.2	66.6	66.9	67.3	67.7	68.1	68.5	68.9	69.2
15	69.6	70.0	70.4	70.7	71.1	71.5	71.9	72.2	72.6	73.0
16	73.3	73.7	74.1	74.4	74.8	75.2	75.5	75.9	76.2	76.6
17	76.9	77.3	77.7	78.0	78.4	78.7	79.1	79.4	79.8	80.1
18	80.5	80.8	81.1	81.5	81.8	82.2	82.5	82.8	83.2	83.5
19	83.9	84.2	84.5	84.9	85.2	85.5	85.9	86.2	86.5	86.8
20	87.2	87.5	87.8	88.1	88.5	88.8	89.1	89.4	89.7	90.1
21	90.4	90.7	91.0	91.3	91.6	91.9	92.2	92.6	92.9	93.2
22	93.5	93.8	94.1	94.4	94.7	95.0	95.3	95.6	95.9	96.2
23	96.5	96.8	97.1	97.4	97.7	97.9	98.2	98.5	98.8	99.1
24	99.4	99.7	100.0	100.2	100.5	100.8	101.1	101.4	101.7	101.9
25	102.2	102.5	102.8	103.0	103.3	103.6	103.9	104.1	104.4	104.7
26	104.9	105.2	105.5	105.7	106.0	106.3	106.5	106.8	107.0	107.3
27	107.6	107.8	108.1	108.3	108.6	108.9	109.1	109.4	109.6	109.9
28	110.1	110.4	110.6	110.9	111.1	111.4	111.6	111.8	112.1	112.3
29	112.6	112.8	113.1	113.3	113.5	113.8	114.0	114.2	114.5	114.7
30	114.9	115.2	115.4	115.6	115.9	116.1	116.3	116.6	116.8	117.0
31	117.2	117.5	117.7	117.9	118.1	118.3	118.6	118.8	119.0	119.2
32	119.4	119.6	119.9	120.1	120.3	120.5	120.7	120.9	121.1	121.3
33	121.6	121.8	122.0	122.2	122.4	122.6	122.8	123.0	123.2	123.4
34	123.6	123.8	124.0	124.2	124.4	124.6	124.8	125.0	125.2	125.4
35	125.6	125.7	125.9	126.1	126.3	126.5	126.7	126.9	127.1	127.3
36	127.4	127.6	127.8	128.0	128.2	128.4	128.5	128.7	128.9	129.1
37	129.3	129.4	129.6	129.8	130.0	130.1	130.3	130.5	130.6	130.8
38	131.0	131.2	131.3	131.5	131.7	131.8	132.0	132.2	132.3	132.5
39	132.7	132.8	133.0	133.1	133.3	133.5	133.6	133.8	133.9	134.1
40	134.2	134.4	134.6	134.7	134.9	135.0	135.2	135.3	135.5	135.6
41	135.8	135.9	136.1	136.2	136.4	136.5	136.7	136.8	136.9	137.1
42	137.2	137.4	137.5	137.6	137.8	137.9	138.1	138.2	138.3	138.5
43	138.6	138.8	138.9	139.0	139.2	139.3	139.4	139.5	139.7	139.8
44	139.9	140.1	140.2	140.3	140.5	140.6	140.7	140.8	141.0	141.1
45	141.2	141.3	141.4	141.6	141.7	141.8	141.9	142.0	142.2	142.3
46	142.4	142.5	142.6	142.7	142.9	143.0	143.1	143.2	143.3	143.4
47	143.5	143.7	143.8	143.9	144.0	144.1	144.2	144.3	144.4	144.5
48	144.6	144.7	144.8	144.9	145.0	145.1	145.2	145.3	145.4	145.5

*See note on page 64 regarding assumptions made in computing this table.

10.16 Metric Rating Table for 60-in. Sacramento Storage Gauge*

Stick Depth cm	Equivalent Precipitation—cm									
	0.0	0.1	0.2	0.3	0.4	0.5	0.6	0.7	0.8	0.9
0	0.0	0.4	0.9	1.3	1.7	2.2	2.6	3.1	3.5	3.9
1	4.3	4.8	5.2	5.6	6.1	6.5	6.9	7.4	7.8	8.2
2	8.6	9.1	9.5	9.9	10.3	10.7	11.2	11.6	12.0	12.4
3	12.8	13.3	13.7	14.1	14.5	14.9	15.3	15.8	16.2	16.6
4	17.0	17.4	17.8	18.2	18.6	19.0	19.4	19.9	20.3	20.7
5	21.1	21.5	21.9	22.3	22.7	23.1	23.5	23.9	24.3	24.7
6	25.1	25.5	25.9	26.3	26.7	27.1	27.5	27.9	28.2	28.6
7	29.0	29.4	29.8	30.2	30.6	31.0	31.4	31.8	32.1	32.5
8	32.9	33.3	33.7	34.1	34.5	34.8	35.2	35.6	36.0	36.4
9	36.7	37.1	37.5	37.9	38.2	38.6	39.0	39.4	39.7	40.1
10	40.5	40.9	41.2	41.6	42.0	42.3	42.7	43.1	43.5	43.8
11	44.2	44.6	44.9	45.3	45.6	46.0	46.4	46.7	47.1	47.5
12	47.8	48.2	48.5	48.9	49.2	49.6	50.0	50.3	50.7	51.0
13	51.4	51.7	52.1	52.4	52.8	53.1	53.5	53.8	54.2	54.5
14	54.9	55.2	55.6	55.9	56.3	56.6	57.0	57.3	57.6	58.0
15	58.3	58.7	59.0	59.4	59.7	60.0	60.4	60.7	61.0	61.4
16	61.7	62.1	62.4	62.7	63.1	63.4	63.7	64.0	64.4	64.7
17	65.0	65.4	65.7	66.0	66.4	66.7	67.0	67.3	67.7	68.0
18	68.3	68.6	68.9	69.3	69.6	69.9	70.2	70.6	70.9	71.2
19	71.5	71.8	72.1	72.5	72.8	73.1	73.4	73.7	74.0	74.3
20	74.7	75.0	75.3	75.6	75.9	76.2	76.5	76.8	77.1	77.4
21	77.7	78.0	78.4	78.7	79.0	79.3	79.6	79.9	80.2	80.5
22	80.8	81.1	81.4	81.7	82.0	82.3	82.6	82.9	83.2	83.5
23	83.7	84.0	84.3	84.6	84.9	85.2	85.5	85.8	86.1	86.4
24	86.7	87.0	87.2	87.5	87.8	88.1	88.4	88.7	89.0	89.2
25	89.5	89.8	90.1	90.4	90.7	90.9	91.2	91.5	91.8	92.1
26	92.3	92.6	92.9	93.2	93.4	93.7	94.0	94.3	94.5	94.8
27	95.1	95.4	95.6	95.9	96.2	96.4	96.7	97.0	97.3	97.5
28	97.8	98.1	98.3	98.6	98.9	99.1	99.4	99.6	99.9	100.2
29	100.4	100.7	101.0	101.2	101.5	101.7	102.0	102.3	102.5	102.8
30	103.0	103.3	103.5	103.8	104.0	104.3	104.6	104.8	105.1	105.3
31	105.6	105.8	106.1	106.3	106.6	106.8	107.1	107.3	107.6	107.8
32	108.0	108.3	108.5	108.8	109.0	109.3	109.5	109.8	110.0	110.2
33	110.5	110.7	111.0	111.2	111.4	111.7	111.9	112.2	112.4	112.6
34	112.9	113.1	113.3	113.6	113.8	114.0	114.3	114.5	114.7	115.0
35	115.2	115.4	115.7	115.9	116.1	116.4	116.6	116.8	117.0	117.3
36	117.5	117.7	117.9	118.2	118.4	118.6	118.8	119.1	119.3	119.5
37	119.7	119.9	120.2	120.4	120.6	120.8	121.0	121.3	121.5	121.7
38	121.9	122.1	122.3	122.6	122.8	123.0	123.2	123.4	123.6	123.8
39	124.0	124.3	124.5	124.7	124.9	125.1	125.3	125.5	125.7	125.9
40	126.1	126.3	126.6	126.8	127.0	127.2	127.4	127.6	127.8	128.0
41	128.2	128.4	128.6	128.8	129.0	129.2	129.4	129.6	129.8	130.0
42	130.2	130.4	130.6	130.8	131.0	131.2	131.4	131.5	131.7	131.9
43	132.1	132.3	132.5	132.7	132.9	133.1	133.3	133.5	133.7	133.8
44	134.0	134.2	134.4	134.6	134.8	135.0	135.2	135.3	135.5	135.7
45	135.9	136.1	136.3	136.4	136.6	136.8	137.0	137.2	137.3	137.5

*See note on page 64 regarding assumptions made in computing this table.

10.16 Metric Rating Table for 60-in. Sacramento Storage Gauge (continued)*

Stick Depth	Equivalent Precipitation—*cm*									
cm	0.0	0.1	0.2	0.3	0.4	0.5	0.6	0.7	0.8	0.9
46	137.7	137.9	138.1	138.2	138.4	138.6	138.8	139.0	139.1	139.3
47	139.5	139.7	139.8	140.0	140.2	140.3	140.5	140.7	140.9	141.0
48	141.2	141.4	141.5	141.7	141.9	142.1	142.2	142.4	142.6	142.7
49	142.9	143.1	143.2	143.4	143.6	143.7	143.9	144.0	144.2	144.4
50	144.5	144.7	144.9	145.0	145.2	145.3	145.5	145.7	145.8	146.0
51	146.1	146.3	146.5	146.6	146.8	146.9	147.1	147.2	147.4	147.5
52	147.7	147.9	148.0	148.2	148.3	148.5	148.6	148.8	148.9	149.1
53	149.2	149.4	149.5	149.7	149.8	150.0	150.1	150.3	150.4	150.5
54	150.7	150.8	151.0	151.1	151.3	151.4	151.6	151.7	151.8	152.0
55	152.1	152.3	152.4	152.6	152.7	152.8	153.0	153.1	153.3	153.4
56	153.5	153.7	153.8	153.9	154.1	154.2	154.4	154.5	154.6	154.8
57	154.9	155.0	155.2	155.3	155.4	155.6	155.7	155.8	156.0	156.1
58	156.2	156.4	156.5	156.6	156.7	156.9	157.0	157.1	157.3	157.4
59	157.5	157.6	157.8	157.9	158.0	158.1	158.3	158.4	158.5	158.6
60	158.8	158.9	159.0	159.1	159.2	159.4	159.5	159.6	159.7	159.8
61	160.0	160.1	160.2	160.3	160.4	160.6	160.7	160.8	160.9	161.0
62	161.1	161.3	161.4	161.5	161.6	161.7	161.8	161.9	162.1	162.2
63	162.3	162.4	162.5	162.6	162.7	162.8	163.0	163.1	163.2	163.3
64	163.4	163.5	163.6	163.7	163.8	163.9	164.0	164.1	164.3	164.4
65	164.5	164.6	164.7	164.8	164.9	165.0	165.1	165.2	165.3	165.4
66	165.5	165.6	165.7	165.8	165.9	166.0	166.1	166.2	166.3	166.4

*See note on page 64 regarding assumptions made in computing this table.

10.17   Metric Rating Table for 100-in. Sacramento Storage Gauge*

Stick Depth	Equivalent Precipitation—*cm*									
cm	0.0	0.1	0.2	0.3	0.4	0.5	0.6	0.7	0.8	0.9
0	0.0	0.6	1.3	1.9	2.6	3.2	3.9	4.5	5.1	5.8
1	6.4	7.0	7.7	8.3	8.9	9.6	10.2	10.8	11.5	12.1
2	12.7	13.4	14.0	14.6	15.2	15.9	16.5	17.1	17.7	18.3
3	19.0	19.6	20.2	20.8	21.4	22.1	22.7	23.3	23.9	24.5
4	25.1	25.7	26.3	27.0	27.6	28.2	28.8	29.4	30.0	30.6
5	31.2	31.8	32.4	33.0	33.6	34.2	34.8	35.4	36.0	36.6
6	37.2	37.8	38.4	39.0	39.6	40.2	40.8	41.3	41.9	42.5
7	43.1	43.7	44.3	44.9	45.5	46.0	46.6	47.2	47.8	48.4
8	49.0	49.5	50.1	50.7	51.3	51.8	52.4	53.0	53.6	54.1
9	54.7	55.3	55.9	56.4	57.0	57.6	58.1	58.7	59.3	59.8
10	60.4	61.0	61.5	62.1	62.6	63.2	63.8	64.3	64.9	65.4
11	66.0	66.5	67.1	67.7	68.2	68.8	69.3	69.9	70.4	71.0
12	71.5	72.1	72.6	73.2	73.7	74.2	74.8	75.3	75.9	76.4
13	77.0	77.5	78.0	78.6	79.1	79.7	80.2	80.7	81.3	81.8
14	82.3	82.9	83.4	83.9	84.5	85.0	85.5	86.0	86.6	87.1
15	87.6	88.2	88.7	89.2	89.7	90.2	90.8	91.3	91.8	92.3
16	92.8	93.4	93.9	94.4	94.9	95.4	95.9	96.5	97.0	97.5
17	98.0	98.5	99.0	99.5	100.0	100.5	101.0	101.6	102.1	102.6
18	103.1	103.6	104.1	104.6	105.1	105.6	106.1	106.6	107.1	107.6
19	108.1	108.6	109.1	109.5	110.0	110.5	111.0	111.5	112.0	112.5
20	113.0	113.5	114.0	114.5	114.9	115.4	115.9	116.4	116.9	117.4
21	117.8	118.3	118.8	119.3	119.8	120.2	120.7	121.2	121.7	122.1
22	122.6	123.1	123.6	124.0	124.5	125.0	125.5	125.9	126.4	126.9
23	127.3	127.8	128.3	128.7	129.2	129.7	130.1	130.6	131.0	131.5
24	132.0	132.4	132.9	133.3	133.8	134.3	134.7	135.2	135.6	136.1
25	136.5	137.0	137.4	137.9	138.3	138.8	139.2	139.7	140.1	140.6
26	141.0	141.5	141.9	142.4	142.8	143.3	143.7	144.1	144.6	145.0
27	145.5	145.9	146.3	146.8	147.2	147.6	148.1	148.5	149.0	149.4
28	149.8	150.3	150.7	151.1	151.5	152.0	152.4	152.8	153.3	153.7
29	154.1	154.5	155.0	155.4	155.8	156.2	156.7	157.1	157.5	157.9
30	158.3	158.8	159.2	159.6	160.0	160.4	160.8	161.2	161.7	162.1
31	162.5	162.9	163.3	163.7	164.1	164.5	165.0	165.4	165.8	166.2
32	166.6	167.0	167.4	167.8	168.2	168.6	169.0	169.4	169.8	170.2
33	170.6	171.0	171.4	171.8	172.2	172.6	173.0	173.4	173.8	174.2
34	174.6	175.0	175.3	175.7	176.1	176.5	176.9	177.3	177.7	178.1
35	178.5	178.8	179.2	179.6	180.0	180.4	180.8	181.1	181.5	181.9
36	182.3	182.7	183.0	183.4	183.8	184.2	184.5	184.9	185.3	185.7
37	186.0	186.4	186.8	187.2	187.5	187.9	188.3	188.6	189.0	189.4
38	189.7	190.1	190.5	190.8	191.2	191.6	191.9	192.3	192.7	193.0
39	193.4	193.7	194.1	194.5	194.8	195.2	195.5	195.9	196.3	196.6
40	197.0	197.3	197.7	198.0	198.4	198.7	199.1	199.4	199.8	200.1
41	200.5	200.8	201.2	201.5	201.9	202.2	202.6	202.9	203.2	203.6
42	203.9	204.3	204.6	205.0	205.3	205.6	206.0	206.3	206.6	207.0
43	207.3	207.7	208.0	208.3	208.7	209.0	209.3	209.7	210.0	210.3
44	210.7	211.0	211.3	211.6	212.0	212.3	212.6	212.9	213.3	213.6
45	213.9	214.2	214.6	214.9	215.2	215.5	215.9	216.2	216.5	216.8

*See note on page 64 regarding assumptions made in computing this table.

10.17 Metric Rating Table for 100-in. Sacramento Storage Gauge (continued)*

Stick Depth	Equivalent Precipitation—*cm*									
cm	0.0	0.1	0.2	0.3	0.4	0.5	0.6	0.7	0.8	0.9
46	217.1	217.5	217.8	218.1	218.4	218.7	219.0	219.4	219.7	220.0
47	220.3	220.6	220.9	221.2	221.5	221.8	222.2	222.5	222.8	223.1
48	223.4	223.7	224.0	224.3	224.6	224.9	225.2	225.5	225.8	226.1
49	226.4	226.7	227.0	227.3	227.6	227.9	228.2	228.5	228.8	229.1
50	229.4	229.7	230.0	230.3	230.6	230.9	231.2	231.5	231.8	232.0
51	232.3	232.6	232.9	233.2	233.5	233.8	234.1	234.4	234.6	234.9
52	235.2	235.5	235.8	236.1	236.3	236.6	236.9	237.2	237.5	237.7
53	238.0	238.3	238.6	238.9	239.1	239.4	239.7	240.0	240.2	240.5
54	240.8	241.1	241.3	241.6	241.9	242.1	242.4	242.7	243.0	243.2
55	243.5	243.8	244.0	244.3	244.6	244.8	245.1	245.4	245.6	245.9
56	246.1	246.4	246.7	246.9	247.2	247.4	247.7	248.0	248.2	248.5
57	248.7	249.0	249.3	249.5	249.8	250.0	250.3	250.5	250.8	251.0
58	251.3	251.5	251.8	252.0	252.3	252.5	252.8	253.0	253.3	253.5
59	253.8	254.0	254.3	254.5	254.8	255.0	255.3	255.5	255.7	256.0
60	256.2	256.5	256.7	256.9	257.2	257.4	257.7	257.9	258.1	258.4
61	258.6	258.9	259.1	259.3	259.6	259.8	260.0	260.3	260.5	260.7
62	261.0	261.2	261.4	261.7	261.9	262.1	262.3	262.6	262.8	263.0
63	263.2	263.5	263.7	263.9	264.2	264.4	264.6	264.8	265.0	265.3
64	265.5	265.7	265.9	266.2	266.4	266.6	266.8	267.0	267.3	267.5
65	267.7	267.9	268.1	268.3	268.5	268.8	269.0	269.2	269.4	269.6
66	269.8	270.0	270.3	270.5	270.7	270.9	271.1	271.3	271.5	271.7
67	271.9	272.1	272.3	272.5	272.8	273.0	273.2	273.4	273.6	273.8
68	274.0	274.2	274.4	274.6	274.8	275.0	275.2	275.4	275.6	275.8
69	276.0	276.2	276.4	276.6	276.8	277.0	277.2	277.4	277.5	277.7
70	277.9	278.1	278.3	278.5	278.7	278.9	279.1	279.3	279.5	279.7
71	279.8	280.0	280.2	280.4	280.6	280.8	281.0	281.2	281.3	281.5
72	281.7	281.9	282.1	282.3	282.4	282.6	282.8	283.0	283.2	283.4
73	283.5	283.7	283.9	284.1	284.3	284.4	284.6	284.8	285.0	285.1
74	285.3	285.5	285.7	285.8	286.0	286.2	286.4	286.5	286.7	286.9
75	287.0	287.2	287.4	287.6	287.7	287.9	288.1	288.2	288.4	288.6
76	288.7	288.9	289.1	289.2	289.4	289.6	289.7	289.9	290.1	290.2
77	290.4	290.6	290.7	290.9	291.0	291.2	291.4	291.5	291.7	291.8
78	292.0	292.2	292.3	292.5	292.6	292.8	292.9	293.1	293.3	293.4
79	293.6	293.7	293.9	294.0	294.2	294.3	294.5	294.6	294.8	294.9
80	295.1	295.2	295.4	295.5	295.7	295.8	296.0	296.1	296.3	296.4
81	296.6	296.7	296.9	297.0	297.2	297.3	297.4	297.6	297.7	297.9
82	298.0	298.2	298.3	298.4	298.6	298.7	298.9	299.0	299.1	299.3
83	299.4	299.6	299.7	299.8	300.0	300.1	300.2	300.4	300.5	300.7
84	300.8	300.9	301.1	301.2	301.3	301.5	301.6	301.7	301.9	302.0
85	302.1	302.2	302.4	302.5	302.6	302.8	302.9	303.0	303.2	303.3
86	303.4	303.5	303.7	303.8	303.9	304.0	304.2	304.3	304.4	304.5
87	304.7	304.8	304.9	305.0	305.2	305.3	305.4	305.5	305.6	305.8
88	305.9	306.0	306.1	306.2	306.4	306.5	306.6	306.7	306.8	306.9
89	307.1	307.2	307.3	307.4	307.5	307.6	307.8	307.9	308.0	308.1
90	308.2	308.3	308.4	308.5	308.7	308.8	308.9	309.0	309.1	309.2

*See note on page 64 regarding assumptions made in computing this table.

10.18   Metric Rating Table for 200-in. Sacramento Storage Gauge*

Stick Depth	Equivalent Precipitation—*cm*									
cm	0.0	0.1	0.2	0.3	0.4	0.5	0.6	0.7	0.8	0.9
0	0.0	1.0	1.9	2.9	3.8	4.7	5.7	6.6	7.6	8.5
1	9.5	10.4	11.4	12.3	13.2	14.2	15.1	16.0	17.0	17.9
2	18.8	19.8	20.7	21.6	22.6	23.5	24.4	25.3	26.3	27.2
3	28.1	29.0	30.0	30.9	31.8	32.7	33.6	34.5	35.5	36.4
4	37.3	38.2	39.1	40.0	40.9	41.8	42.7	43.7	44.6	45.5
5	46.4	47.3	48.2	49.1	50.0	50.9	51.8	52.7	53.6	54.4
6	55.3	56.2	57.1	58.0	58.9	59.8	60.7	61.6	62.4	63.3
7	64.2	65.1	66.0	66.9	67.7	68.6	69.5	70.4	71.2	72.1
8	73.0	73.9	74.7	75.6	76.5	77.3	78.2	79.1	79.9	80.8
9	81.7	82.5	83.4	84.3	85.1	86.0	86.8	87.7	88.6	89.4
10	90.3	91.1	92.0	92.8	93.7	94.5	95.4	96.2	97.1	97.9
11	98.8	99.6	100.4	101.3	102.1	103.0	103.8	104.6	105.5	106.3
12	107.1	108.0	108.8	109.6	110.5	111.3	112.1	113.0	113.8	114.6
13	115.4	116.3	117.1	117.9	118.7	119.6	120.4	121.2	122.0	122.8
14	123.7	124.5	125.3	126.1	126.9	127.7	128.5	129.3	130.1	131.0
15	131.8	132.6	133.4	134.2	135.0	135.8	136.6	137.4	138.2	139.0
16	139.8	140.6	141.4	142.2	143.0	143.8	144.5	145.3	146.1	146.9
17	147.7	148.5	149.3	150.1	150.9	151.6	152.4	153.2	154.0	154.8
18	155.5	156.3	157.1	157.9	158.7	159.4	160.2	161.0	161.7	162.5
19	163.3	164.1	164.8	165.6	166.4	167.1	167.9	168.7	169.4	170.2
20	170.9	171.7	172.5	173.2	174.0	174.7	175.5	176.2	177.0	177.7
21	178.5	179.2	180.0	180.7	181.5	182.2	183.0	183.7	184.5	185.2
22	186.0	186.7	187.5	188.2	188.9	189.7	190.4	191.1	191.9	192.6
23	193.3	194.1	194.8	195.5	196.3	197.0	197.7	198.5	199.2	199.9
24	200.6	201.4	202.1	202.8	203.5	204.3	205.0	205.7	206.4	207.1
25	207.8	208.6	209.3	210.0	210.7	211.4	212.1	212.8	213.5	214.3
26	215.0	215.7	216.4	217.1	217.8	218.5	219.2	219.9	220.6	221.3
27	222.0	222.7	223.4	224.1	224.8	225.5	226.2	226.9	227.6	228.2
28	228.9	229.6	230.3	231.0	231.7	232.4	233.1	233.7	234.4	235.1
29	235.8	236.5	237.2	237.8	238.5	239.2	239.9	240.5	241.2	241.9
30	242.6	243.2	243.9	244.6	245.2	245.9	246.6	247.3	247.9	248.6
31	249.2	249.9	250.6	251.2	251.9	252.6	253.2	253.9	254.5	255.2
32	255.8	256.5	257.2	257.8	258.5	259.1	259.8	260.4	261.1	261.7
33	262.4	263.0	263.7	264.3	265.0	265.6	266.2	266.9	267.5	268.2
34	268.8	269.4	270.1	270.7	271.4	272.0	272.6	273.3	273.9	274.5
35	275.2	275.8	276.4	277.0	277.7	278.3	278.9	279.5	280.2	280.8
36	281.4	282.0	282.7	283.3	283.9	284.5	285.1	285.8	286.4	287.0
37	287.6	288.2	288.8	289.4	290.1	290.7	291.3	291.9	292.5	293.1
38	293.7	294.3	294.9	295.5	296.1	296.7	297.3	297.9	298.5	299.1
39	299.7	300.3	300.9	301.5	302.1	302.7	303.3	303.9	304.5	305.1
40	305.7	306.3	306.9	307.4	308.0	308.6	309.2	309.8	310.4	311.0

*See note on page 64 regarding assumptions made in computing this table.

10.18 Metric Rating Table for 200-in. Sacramento Storage Gauge (continued)*

Stick Depth cm	Equivalent Precipitation—cm									
	0.0	0.1	0.2	0.3	0.4	0.5	0.6	0.7	0.8	0.9
41	311.5	312.1	312.7	313.3	313.9	314.4	315.0	315.6	316.2	316.8
42	317.3	317.9	318.5	319.0	319.6	320.2	320.8	321.3	321.9	322.5
43	323.0	323.6	324.2	324.7	325.3	325.9	326.4	327.0	327.5	328.1
44	328.7	329.2	329.8	330.3	330.9	331.4	332.0	332.6	333.1	333.7
45	334.2	334.8	335.3	335.9	336.4	337.0	337.5	338.1	338.6	339.1
46	339.7	340.2	340.8	341.3	341.9	342.4	342.9	343.5	344.0	344.5
47	345.1	345.6	346.2	346.7	347.2	347.8	348.3	348.8	349.3	349.9
48	350.4	350.9	351.5	352.0	352.5	353.0	353.6	354.1	354.6	355.1
49	355.7	356.2	356.7	357.2	357.7	358.2	358.8	359.3	359.8	360.3
50	360.8	361.3	361.8	362.4	362.9	363.4	363.9	364.4	364.9	365.4
51	365.9	366.4	366.9	367.4	367.9	368.4	368.9	369.4	369.9	370.4
52	370.9	371.4	371.9	372.4	372.9	373.4	373.9	374.4	374.9	375.4
53	375.9	376.4	376.9	377.4	377.9	378.3	378.8	379.3	379.8	380.3
54	380.8	381.3	381.7	382.2	382.7	383.2	383.7	384.1	384.6	385.1
55	385.6	386.1	386.5	387.0	387.5	388.0	388.4	388.9	389.4	389.8
56	390.3	390.8	391.2	391.7	392.2	392.6	393.1	393.6	394.0	394.5
57	395.0	395.4	395.9	396.4	396.8	397.3	397.7	398.2	398.6	399.1
58	399.6	400.0	400.5	400.9	401.4	401.8	402.3	402.7	403.2	403.6
59	404.1	404.5	405.0	405.4	405.9	406.3	406.8	407.2	407.6	408.1
60	408.5	409.0	409.4	409.9	410.3	410.7	411.2	411.6	412.0	412.5
61	412.9	413.4	413.8	414.2	414.7	415.1	415.5	415.9	416.4	416.8
62	417.2	417.7	418.1	418.5	418.9	419.4	419.8	420.2	420.6	421.1
63	421.5	421.9	422.3	422.7	423.2	423.6	424.0	424.4	424.8	425.2
64	425.7	426.1	426.5	426.9	427.3	427.7	428.1	428.5	429.0	429.4
65	429.8	430.2	430.6	431.0	431.4	431.8	432.2	432.6	433.0	433.4
66	433.8	434.2	434.6	435.0	435.4	435.8	436.2	436.6	437.0	437.4
67	437.8	438.2	438.6	439.0	439.4	439.8	440.2	440.5	440.9	441.3
68	441.7	442.1	442.5	442.9	443.3	443.6	444.0	444.4	444.8	445.2
69	445.6	445.9	446.3	446.7	447.1	447.5	447.8	448.2	448.6	449.0
70	449.4	449.7	450.1	450.5	450.8	451.2	451.6	452.0	452.3	452.7
71	453.1	453.4	453.8	454.2	454.5	454.9	455.3	455.6	456.0	456.4
72	456.7	457.1	457.5	457.8	458.2	458.5	458.9	459.3	459.6	460.0
73	460.3	460.7	461.0	461.4	461.8	462.1	462.5	462.8	463.2	463.5
74	463.9	464.2	464.6	464.9	465.3	465.6	466.0	466.3	466.7	467.0
75	467.3	467.7	468.0	468.4	468.7	469.1	469.4	469.7	470.1	470.4
76	470.8	471.1	471.4	471.8	472.1	472.4	472.8	473.1	473.4	473.8
77	474.1	474.4	474.8	475.1	475.4	475.8	476.1	476.4	476.7	477.1
78	477.4	477.7	478.1	478.4	478.7	479.0	479.3	479.7	480.0	480.3
79	480.6	481.0	481.3	481.6	481.9	482.2	482.5	482.9	483.2	483.5
80	483.8	484.1	484.4	484.7	485.1	485.4	485.7	486.0	486.3	486.6

*See note on page 64 regarding assumptions made in computing this table.

10.18   Metric Rating Table for 200-in. Sacramento Storage Gauge (continued)*

Stick Depth	Equivalent Precipitation—cm									
cm	0.0	0.1	0.2	0.3	0.4	0.5	0.6	0.7	0.8	0.9
81	486.9	487.2	487.5	487.8	488.2	488.5	488.8	489.1	489.4	489.7
82	490.0	490.3	490.6	490.9	491.2	491.5	491.8	492.1	492.4	492.7
83	493.0	493.3	493.6	493.9	494.2	494.5	494.8	495.1	495.3	495.6
84	495.9	496.2	496.5	496.8	497.1	497.4	497.7	498.0	498.2	498.5
85	498.8	499.1	499.4	499.7	500.0	500.2	500.5	500.8	501.1	501.4
86	501.7	501.9	502.2	502.5	502.8	503.1	503.3	503.6	503.9	504.2
87	504.4	504.7	505.0	505.3	505.5	505.8	506.1	506.3	506.6	506.9
88	507.2	507.4	507.7	508.0	508.2	508.5	508.8	509.0	509.3	509.6
89	509.8	510.1	510.4	510.6	510.9	511.1	511.4	511.7	511.9	512.2
90	512.4	512.7	513.0	513.2	513.5	513.7	514.0	514.2	514.5	514.8
91	515.0	515.3	515.5	515.8	516.0	516.3	516.5	516.8	517.0	517.3
92	517.5	517.8	518.0	518.3	518.5	518.8	519.0	519.3	519.5	519.7
93	520.0	520.2	520.5	520.7	521.0	521.2	521.4	521.7	521.9	522.2
94	522.4	522.6	522.9	523.1	523.3	523.6	523.8	524.1	524.3	524.5
95	524.8	525.0	525.2	525.5	525.7	525.9	526.1	526.4	526.6	526.8
96	527.1	527.3	527.5	527.7	528.0	528.2	528.4	528.6	528.9	529.1
97	529.3	529.5	529.8	530.0	530.2	530.4	530.7	530.9	531.1	531.3
98	531.5	531.7	532.0	532.2	532.4	532.6	532.8	533.0	533.3	533.5
99	533.7	533.9	534.1	534.3	534.5	534.8	535.0	535.2	535.4	535.6
100	535.8	536.0	536.2	536.4	536.6	536.8	537.1	537.3	537.5	537.7
101	537.9	538.1	538.3	538.5	538.7	538.9	539.1	539.3	539.5	539.7
102	539.9	540.1	540.3	540.5	540.7	540.9	541.1	541.3	541.5	541.7
103	541.9	542.1	542.3	542.4	542.6	542.8	543.0	543.2	543.4	543.6
104	543.8	544.0	544.2	544.4	544.5	544.7	544.9	545.1	545.3	545.5
105	545.7	545.9	546.0	546.2	546.4	546.6	546.8	547.0	547.1	547.3
106	547.5	547.7	547.9	548.1	548.2	548.4	548.6	548.8	548.9	549.1
107	549.3	549.5	549.7	549.8	550.0	550.2	550.4	550.5	550.7	550.9
108	551.1	551.2	551.4	551.6	551.7	551.9	552.1	552.2	552.4	552.6
109	552.8	552.9	553.1	553.3	553.4	553.6	553.8	553.9	554.1	554.3
110	554.4	554.6	554.7	554.9	555.1	555.2	555.4	555.6	555.7	555.9
111	556.0	556.2	556.4	556.5	556.7	556.8	557.0	557.2	557.3	557.5
112	557.6	557.8	557.9	558.1	558.2	558.4	558.6	558.7	558.9	559.0
113	559.2	559.3	559.5	559.6	559.8	559.9	560.1	560.2	560.4	560.5
114	560.7	560.8	561.0	561.1	561.2	561.4	561.5	561.7	561.8	562.0
115	562.1	562.3	562.4	562.5	562.7	562.8	563.0	563.1	563.3	563.4
116	563.5	563.7	563.8	564.0	564.1	564.2	564.4	564.5	564.6	564.8
117	564.9	565.1	565.2	565.3	565.5	565.6	565.7	565.9	566.0	566.1
118	566.3	566.4	566.5	566.7	566.8	566.9	567.0	567.2	567.3	567.4
119	567.6	567.7	567.8	567.9	568.1	568.2	568.3	568.5	568.6	568.7
120	568.8	569.0	569.1	569.2	569.3	569.5	569.6	569.7	569.8	569.9

*See note on page 64 regarding assumptions made in computing this table.

10.19 Metric Rating Table for 300-in. Sacramento Storage Gauge*

Stick Depth cm	Equivalent Precipitation—cm									
	0.0	0.1	0.2	0.3	0.4	0.5	0.6	0.7	0.8	0.9
0	0.0	1.3	2.5	3.8	5.0	6.2	7.5	8.7	10.0	11.2
1	12.5	13.7	14.9	16.2	17.4	18.7	19.9	21.1	22.4	23.6
2	24.8	26.0	27.3	28.5	29.7	30.9	32.2	33.4	34.6	35.8
3	37.1	38.3	39.5	40.7	41.9	43.1	44.3	45.6	46.8	48.0
4	49.2	50.4	51.6	52.8	54.0	55.2	56.4	57.6	58.8	60.0
5	61.2	62.4	63.6	64.8	66.0	67.1	68.3	69.5	70.7	71.9
6	73.1	74.3	75.4	76.6	77.8	79.0	80.2	81.3	82.5	83.7
7	84.9	86.0	87.2	88.4	89.5	90.7	91.9	93.0	94.2	95.4
8	96.5	97.7	98.8	100.0	101.2	102.3	103.5	104.6	105.8	106.9
9	108.1	109.2	110.4	111.5	112.7	113.8	115.0	116.1	117.2	118.4
10	119.5	120.7	121.8	122.9	124.1	125.2	126.3	127.5	128.6	129.7
11	130.9	132.0	133.1	134.2	135.4	136.5	137.6	138.7	139.9	141.0
12	142.1	143.2	144.3	145.4	146.5	147.7	148.8	149.9	151.0	152.1
13	153.2	154.3	155.4	156.5	157.6	158.7	159.8	160.9	162.0	163.1
14	164.2	165.3	166.4	167.5	168.6	169.7	170.8	171.9	172.9	174.0
15	175.1	176.2	177.3	178.4	179.4	180.5	181.6	182.7	183.7	184.8
16	185.9	187.0	188.0	189.1	190.2	191.3	192.3	193.4	194.5	195.5
17	196.6	197.6	198.7	199.8	200.8	201.9	202.9	204.0	205.0	206.1
18	207.2	208.2	209.3	210.3	211.4	212.4	213.4	214.5	215.5	216.6
19	217.6	218.7	219.7	220.7	221.8	222.8	223.9	224.9	225.9	227.0
20	228.0	229.0	230.0	231.1	232.1	233.1	234.2	235.2	236.2	237.2
21	238.2	239.3	240.3	241.3	242.3	243.3	244.3	245.4	246.4	247.4
22	248.4	249.4	250.4	251.4	252.4	253.4	254.4	255.4	256.4	257.4
23	258.4	259.4	260.4	261.4	262.4	263.4	264.4	265.4	266.4	267.4
24	268.4	269.4	270.4	271.4	272.3	273.3	274.3	275.3	276.3	277.3
25	278.2	279.2	280.2	281.2	282.1	283.1	284.1	285.1	286.0	287.0
26	288.0	288.9	289.9	290.9	291.8	292.8	293.8	294.7	295.7	296.6
27	297.6	298.6	299.5	300.5	301.4	302.4	303.3	304.3	305.2	306.2
28	307.1	308.1	309.0	310.0	310.9	311.9	312.8	313.8	314.7	315.6
29	316.6	317.5	318.4	319.4	320.3	321.3	322.2	323.1	324.0	325.0
30	325.9	326.8	327.8	328.7	329.6	330.5	331.5	332.4	333.3	334.2
31	335.1	336.1	337.0	337.9	338.8	339.7	340.6	341.5	342.5	343.4
32	344.3	345.2	346.1	347.0	347.9	348.8	349.7	350.6	351.5	352.4
33	353.3	354.2	355.1	356.0	356.9	357.8	358.7	359.6	360.5	361.4
34	362.2	363.1	364.0	364.9	365.8	366.7	367.6	368.4	369.3	370.2
35	371.1	372.0	372.8	373.7	374.6	375.5	376.3	377.2	378.1	379.0
36	379.8	380.7	381.6	382.4	383.3	384.2	385.0	385.9	386.8	387.6
37	388.5	389.3	390.2	391.0	391.9	392.8	393.6	394.5	395.3	396.2
38	397.0	397.9	398.7	399.6	400.4	401.3	402.1	403.0	403.8	404.6
39	405.5	406.3	407.2	408.0	408.8	409.7	410.5	411.3	412.2	413.0
40	413.8	414.7	415.5	416.3	417.2	418.0	418.8	419.6	420.5	421.3

*See note on page 64 regarding assumptions made in computing this table.

10.19 Metric Rating Table for 300-in. Sacramento Storage Gauge (continued)*

Stick Depth cm	Equivalent Precipitation—cm									
	0.0	0.1	0.2	0.3	0.4	0.5	0.6	0.7	0.8	0.9
41	422.1	422.9	423.7	424.6	425.4	426.2	427.0	427.8	428.6	429.5
42	430.3	431.1	431.9	432.7	433.5	434.3	435.1	435.9	436.7	437.5
43	438.3	439.1	439.9	440.7	441.5	442.3	443.1	443.9	444.7	445.5
44	446.3	447.1	447.9	448.7	449.5	450.3	451.1	451.9	452.6	453.4
45	454.2	455.0	455.8	456.6	457.3	458.1	458.9	459.7	460.5	461.2
46	462.0	462.8	463.6	464.3	465.1	465.9	466.7	467.4	468.2	469.0
47	469.7	470.5	471.3	472.0	472.8	473.5	474.3	475.1	475.8	476.6
48	477.3	478.1	478.9	479.6	480.4	481.1	481.9	482.6	483.4	484.1
49	484.9	485.6	486.4	487.1	487.9	488.6	489.3	490.1	490.8	491.6
50	492.3	493.0	493.8	494.5	495.3	496.0	496.7	497.5	498.2	498.9
51	499.6	500.4	501.1	501.8	502.6	503.3	504.0	504.7	505.5	506.2
52	506.9	507.6	508.3	509.1	509.8	510.5	511.2	511.9	512.7	513.4
53	514.1	514.8	515.5	516.2	516.9	517.6	518.3	519.0	519.8	520.5
54	521.2	521.9	522.6	523.3	524.0	524.7	525.4	526.1	526.8	527.5
55	528.2	528.9	529.5	530.2	530.9	531.6	532.3	533.0	533.7	534.4
56	535.1	535.8	536.4	537.1	537.8	538.5	539.2	539.9	540.5	541.2
57	541.9	542.6	543.2	543.9	544.6	545.3	545.9	546.6	547.3	548.0
58	548.6	549.3	550.0	550.6	551.3	552.0	552.6	553.3	554.0	554.6
59	555.3	555.9	556.6	557.3	557.9	558.6	559.2	559.9	560.5	561.2
60	561.9	562.5	563.2	563.8	564.5	565.1	565.8	566.4	567.0	567.7
61	568.3	569.0	569.6	570.3	570.9	571.5	572.2	572.8	573.5	574.1
62	574.7	575.4	576.0	576.6	577.3	577.9	578.5	579.2	579.8	580.4
63	581.1	581.7	582.3	582.9	583.6	584.2	584.8	585.4	586.1	586.7
64	587.3	587.9	588.5	589.1	589.8	590.4	591.0	591.6	592.2	592.8
65	593.4	594.1	594.7	595.3	595.9	596.5	597.1	597.7	598.3	598.9
66	599.5	600.1	600.7	601.3	601.9	602.5	603.1	603.7	604.3	604.9
67	605.5	606.1	606.7	607.3	607.9	608.5	609.1	609.7	610.3	610.8
68	611.4	612.0	612.6	613.2	613.8	614.4	614.9	615.5	616.1	616.7
69	617.3	617.8	618.4	619.0	619.6	620.1	620.7	621.3	621.9	622.4
70	623.0	623.6	624.2	624.7	625.3	625.9	626.4	627.0	627.6	628.1
71	628.7	629.3	629.8	630.4	630.9	631.5	632.1	632.6	633.2	633.7
72	634.3	634.8	635.4	636.0	636.5	637.1	637.6	638.2	638.7	639.3
73	639.8	640.4	640.9	641.5	642.0	642.5	643.1	643.6	644.2	644.7
74	645.3	645.8	646.3	646.9	647.4	648.0	648.5	649.0	649.6	650.1
75	650.6	651.2	651.7	652.2	652.8	653.3	653.8	654.3	654.9	655.4
76	655.9	656.4	657.0	657.5	658.0	658.5	659.1	659.6	660.1	660.6
77	661.1	661.7	662.2	662.7	663.2	663.7	664.2	664.7	665.3	665.8
78	666.3	666.8	667.3	667.8	668.3	668.8	669.3	669.8	670.3	670.8
79	671.3	671.8	672.3	672.9	673.4	673.9	674.4	674.8	675.3	675.8
80	676.3	676.8	677.3	677.8	678.3	678.8	679.3	679.8	680.3	680.8

*See note on page 64 regarding assumptions made in computing this table.

10.19   Metric Rating Table for 300-in. Sacramento Storage Gauge (continued)*

Stick Depth	Equivalent Precipitation—*cm*									
cm	0.0	0.1	0.2	0.3	0.4	0.5	0.6	0.7	0.8	0.9
81	681.3	681.7	682.2	682.7	683.2	683.7	684.2	684.7	685.1	685.6
82	686.1	686.6	687.1	687.6	688.0	688.5	689.0	689.5	689.9	690.4
83	690.9	691.4	691.8	692.3	692.8	693.2	693.7	694.2	694.7	695.1
84	695.6	696.1	696.5	697.0	697.5	697.9	698.4	698.8	699.3	699.8
85	700.2	700.7	701.1	701.6	702.1	702.5	703.0	703.4	703.9	704.3
86	704.8	705.2	705.7	706.1	706.6	707.0	707.5	707.9	708.4	708.8
87	709.3	709.7	710.2	710.6	711.1	711.5	711.9	712.4	712.8	713.3
88	713.7	714.2	714.6	715.0	715.5	715.9	716.3	716.8	717.2	717.6
89	718.1	718.5	718.9	719.4	719.8	720.2	720.6	721.1	721.5	721.9
90	722.4	722.8	723.2	723.6	724.1	724.5	724.9	725.3	725.7	726.2
91	726.6	727.0	727.4	727.8	728.2	728.7	729.1	729.5	729.9	730.3
92	730.7	731.1	731.6	732.0	732.4	732.8	733.2	733.6	734.0	734.4
93	734.8	735.2	735.6	736.0	736.4	736.8	737.2	737.6	738.0	738.4
94	738.8	739.2	739.6	740.0	740.4	740.8	741.2	741.6	742.0	742.4
95	742.8	743.2	743.6	744.0	744.4	744.7	745.1	745.5	745.9	746.3
96	746.7	747.1	747.5	747.8	748.2	748.6	749.0	749.4	749.8	750.1
97	750.5	750.9	751.3	751.6	752.0	752.4	752.8	753.2	753.5	753.9
98	754.3	754.6	755.0	755.4	755.8	756.1	756.5	756.9	757.2	757.6
99	758.0	758.3	758.7	759.1	759.4	759.8	760.2	760.5	760.9	761.2
100	761.6	762.0	762.3	762.7	763.0	763.4	763.8	764.1	764.5	764.8
101	765.2	765.5	765.9	766.2	766.6	766.9	767.3	767.6	768.0	768.3
102	768.7	769.0	769.4	769.7	770.1	770.4	770.8	771.1	771.5	771.8
103	772.1	772.5	772.8	773.2	773.5	773.8	774.2	774.5	774.9	775.2
104	775.5	775.9	776.2	776.5	776.9	777.2	777.5	777.9	778.2	778.5
105	778.9	779.2	779.5	779.8	780.2	780.5	780.8	781.2	781.5	781.8
106	782.1	782.5	782.8	783.1	783.4	783.7	784.1	784.4	784.7	785.0
107	785.3	785.7	786.0	786.3	786.6	786.9	787.2	787.6	787.9	788.2
108	788.5	788.8	789.1	789.4	789.7	790.1	790.4	790.7	791.0	791.3
109	791.6	791.9	792.2	792.5	792.8	793.1	793.4	793.7	794.0	794.3
110	794.6	794.9	795.2	795.5	795.8	796.1	796.4	796.7	797.0	797.3
111	797.6	797.9	798.2	798.5	798.8	799.1	799.4	799.7	800.0	800.2
112	800.5	800.8	801.1	801.4	801.7	802.0	802.3	802.5	802.8	803.1
113	803.4	803.7	804.0	804.2	804.5	804.8	805.1	805.4	805.7	805.9
114	806.2	806.5	806.8	807.0	807.3	807.6	807.9	808.1	808.4	808.7
115	809.0	809.2	809.5	809.8	810.1	810.3	810.6	810.9	811.1	811.4
116	811.7	811.9	812.2	812.5	812.7	813.0	813.3	813.5	813.8	814.1
117	814.3	814.6	814.8	815.1	815.4	815.6	815.9	816.1	816.4	816.7
118	816.9	817.2	817.4	817.7	817.9	818.2	818.5	818.7	819.0	819.2
119	819.5	819.7	820.0	820.2	820.5	820.7	821.0	821.2	821.5	821.7
120	822.0	822.2	822.5	822.7	822.9	823.2	823.4	823.7	823.9	824.2

*See note on page 64 regarding assumptions made in computing this table.

11

Hydraulic Formulas and Tables

11.1   Weir Formulas

Basic Formula: The basic formula for weirs is:

$$Q = C L H^n$$

Where: Q = discharge
C = discharge coefficient
L = crest length
H = head above crest
n = exponent, which depends on geometry of weir.

Refer to Figure 5 for weir configurations.

Contracted Rectangular Weirs: The formula for contracted rectangular weirs is:

$$Q = 3.33 \, H^{1.5} \, (L - 0.2H)$$

Where: approach velocities are negligible
L and H are in ft
Q is in cfs.

or

$$Q = 3.33 \, [(H + h)^{1.5} - h^{1.5}] \, (L - 0.2H)$$

Where: h = $v^2/2g$ = head due to velocity of approach, v
g = gravitational constant
All other terms remain the same.

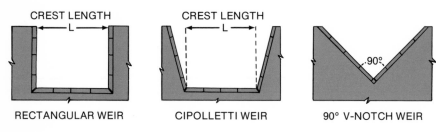

CREST LENGTH   CREST LENGTH

RECTANGULAR WEIR   CIPOLLETTI WEIR   90° V-NOTCH WEIR

Figure 5   Standard Contracted Weir Shapes

Suppressed Rectangular Weirs: The formula for suppressed rectangular weirs is:

$$Q = 3.33 \, L \, H^{1.5}$$

for negligible approach velocities; or

$$Q = 3.33 \, L \, [(H + h)^{1.5} - h^{1.5}]$$

Where: terms are as defined above.

NOTE: The above equations for rectangular weirs are valid only for $H \geq 0.2$ ft.

Cipolletti Weirs: The formula for Cipolletti weirs with 4:1 sides is:

$$Q = 3.367 \, L \, H^{1.5}$$

for negligible approach velocities; or

$$Q = 3.367 \, L \, (H + 1.5h)^{1.5}$$

Where: terms are as defined above.

The velocity of approach, v, may be computed as:

$$v = Q/A$$

Where: A = cross-sectional area of approach channel or weir box, ft^2
Q = discharge as estimated by the appropriate weir formula or from tables without the velocity of approach.

Triangular Weirs: The basic equation for flow through triangular weirs is:

$$Q = C' \tan(\alpha/2) \, H^{2.5}$$

Where: Q = discharge, cfs
$C' = 8/15 \sqrt{2g} \, C_d$
C_d = correction coefficient
α = V-notch angle, degrees
H = head above lowest point of V-notch, ft
g = gravitational constant, ft/s^2.

C_d varies with both head and angle of the V-notch and is best determined experimentally where a high degree of accuracy is desired. See Brater and King (1976) for a more detailed discussion.

A more useful form of the triangular weir formula is:

$$Q = C H^{2.5}$$

Where: values of C for various V-notch angles and for various heads are given in the following table.

Values of C for Triangular Weir Formula

| Head | Angle of V-notch—*degrees* | | | | | |
ft	22.5	30	45	60	90	120
0.5	0.520	0.693	1.056	1.457	2.497	4.303
1.0	0.505	0.676	1.034	1.432	2.463	4.259
1.5	0.499	0.668	1.024	1.420	2.446	4.237
2.0	0.496	0.665	1.020	1.415	2.442	4.229
2.5	0.494	0.663	1.018	1.412	2.437	4.222
3.0	0.493	0.662	1.017	1.410	2.437	4.222

The formula for a compound weir (contracted rectangular weir with an incised 90° V-notch) is:

$$Q = 3.9\, H^{1.72} - 1.5 + 3.3\, L\, h^{1.5}$$

Where: Q = discharge, cfs
H = head above point of V-notch, ft
L = combined length of horizontal sections of weir, ft
h = head above crest (horizontal), ft.

The formula for a Columbus-type control (see Figure 6) is:

$$Q = 8.5\, (H - 0.2)^{3.3}$$

Terms were defined previously.

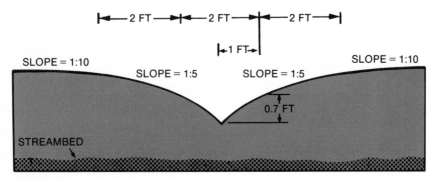

Figure 6   Columbus Control

The basic formula for a broad-crested rectangular weir is:

$$Q = C L (H + h)^{1.5}$$

Where: C, L, and H were defined previously and h is the velocity head.

The discharge coefficient, C, varies between 2.6 and 3.7, depending on head, height of crest above approach channel, and slope of upstream face. At heads below 3.0 ft, C will nearly always be between 2.6 and 3.0. See Rantz (1982) and Brater and King (1976) for complete discussions on discharge coefficients.

11.2   Flume Formulas

H, HS, HL Flumes: Flume head-discharge relationships are normally developed from laboratory calibrations. Rating tables for H-type, HS-type, and HL-type flumes are found in US Department of Agriculture (1979).

Parshall Flumes: The general formula for large ($W > 8$ ft) Parshall flumes is:

$$Q = (3.6875 \ W + 2.5) \ H_a^{1.6}$$

Where: Q = discharge, cfs
W = throat width, ft
H_a = upper gauge head.

The formula for Parshall flumes carrying flows <60 cfs is:

$$Q = 4.0 \ W \ H_a^{1.522W^{0.026}}$$

The formula for Parshall flumes carrying flows 60–1500 cfs is:

$$Q = 3.75 \ W \ H_a^{1.6}$$

In the above Parshall flume equations, H_a is measured $2/3(W/2 + 4)$ ft back from the crest.

11.3   Capacities and Sensitivities of Weirs

Weir Type	Q at $H = 0.2$ ft cfs	Q at $H = 3.0$ ft cfs	Q Response to 0.01 ft Change in H cfs
Contracted Rectangular			
$L = $ 2 ft	0.6	24.2	0.09
$L = $ 5 ft	1.5	76.1	0.28
$L = 10$ ft	3.0	162.6	0.58
$L = 20$ ft	5.9	335.7	1.19
Suppressed Rectangular			
$L = $ 2 ft	0.6	34.6	0.12
$L = $ 5 ft	1.5	86.5	0.31
$L = 10$ ft	3.0	173.0	0.61
$L = 20$ ft	6.0	346.1	1.23
Cipolletti			
$L = $ 2 ft	0.6	35.0	0.12
$L = $ 5 ft	1.5	87.5	0.31
$L = 10$ ft	3.0	175.0	0.62
$L = 20$ ft	6.0	349.9	1.24
Triangular			
30°	0.01	10.3	0.03
60°	0.03	22.0	0.07
90°	0.04	38.0	0.11
120°	0.08	65.8	0.20
Broad-crested			
$C = 2.6, L = 5$	1.2	67.5	0.24
$C = 2.6, L = 20$	4.7	270.2	0.96
$C = 3.0, L = 5$	1.3	77.9	0.28
$C = 3.0, L = 20$	5.4	311.8	1.10

NOTE: Negligible approach velocity is assumed in this table.

11.4   Capacities of Standard Parshall Flumes*

Throat Width in.	Distance From Crest, H_a ft	Free Flow Capacities	
		Min. cfs	Max. cfs
1	0.79	0.005	0.15
2	0.91	0.01	0.30
3	1.02	0.03	1.90
6	1.36	0.05	3.90
9	1.93	0.09	8.90
ft	ft	cfs	cfs
1	3.00	0.11	16.1
1.5	3.17	0.15	24.6
2	3.33	0.42	33.1
3	3.67	0.61	50.4
4	4.00	1.30	67.9
5	4.33	1.60	85.6
6	4.67	2.60	103.5
7	5.00	3.00	121.4
8	5.33	3.50	139.5
10	6.00	6.0	300
12	6.67	8.0	520
15	7.67	8.0	900
20	9.33	10	1340
25	11.00	15	1660
30	12.67	15	1990
40	16.00	20	2640
50	19.33	25	3280

*From Rantz (1982)

11.5   Capacities and Sensitivities of H Flumes

Depth ft	Q at $H = 0.2$ ft cfs	Capacity cfs	Change in Q with 0.01 ft Change in Head cfs
HS Type			
0.4	0.0179	0.085	0.0021
0.6	0.0207	0.23	0.0035
0.8	0.0237	0.47	0.006
1.0	0.0270	0.82	0.007
H Type			
0.5	0.0431	0.35	0.0063
0.75	0.0501	0.96	0.011
1	0.0571	1.96	0.018
1.5	0.0711	5.41	0.033
2	0.0850	11.1	0.05
2.5	0.0990	19.3	0.07
3	0.113	30.6	0.09
4.5	0.155	84.5	0.2
HL Type			
4	0.278	117	0.3

11.6   Formulas for Contracted Openings and Overflow Spillways _____

Stream-Channel Contractions: Discharge through a contraction of a stream channel, such as a bridge section, can be estimated using:

$$Q = C\,W\,H^{1.5}$$

Where: Q = discharge, cfs
W = width of opening, ft
H = head measured from floor of contraction, ft
C = discharge coefficient.

Discharge coefficients vary with geometry of the contraction. A value of 0.95 can be used for rough approximations of Q. See US Department of Agriculture (1979) for a complete discussion.

Overflow Spillways: Overflow spillways usually behave as weirs. The general equation is:

$$Q = C\,W\,(H + h)^{n}$$

Where: Q = discharge, cfs
C = discharge coefficient
W = width of spillway normal to flow, ft
H = head above crest, ft
h = mean velocity head in approach section, ft/s
n = exponent related to spillway crest geometry.

If the spillway crest resembles a broad-crested rectangular weir, a value of 3.7 should be used for C and 1.5 for n. If the spillway is round-crested, a value of $C = 3.4$ can be used for heads below 3.0 ft. Refer to Hulsing (1976) for more information on discharge coefficients. For spillway crests having a swale profile, a value of 3.5 should be used for C; a value of $n = 1.65$ should be used for shallow swales, and $n = 2.5$ should be used for spillways having a nearly triangular profile.

11.7 Flow From Horizontal Pipes —————————————————————————

The discharge from horizontal pipes flowing full (Figure 7) can be approximated using the following formula:

$$Q = \frac{2.45 \, d^2 \, x}{\sqrt{2 \, y/g}}$$

Where: d = pipe diameter, in.
  x = horizontal distance, ft
  y = vertical distance, ft
  g = gravitational constant.

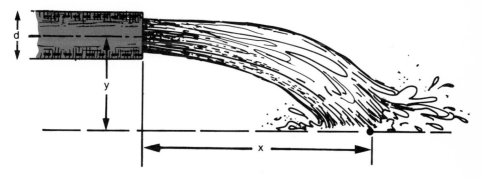

Figure 7   Flow From a Horizontal Pipe

11.8   Design Discharges (cfs) for Broad-Crested Rectangular Weirs (C = 3.7)

Head	Spillway Width—ft									
ft	2	4	6	8	10	12	14	16	18	20
0.1	0.2	0.5	0.7	0.9	1.2	1.4	1.6	1.9	2.1	2.3
0.2	0.7	1.3	2.0	2.6	3.3	4.0	4.6	5.3	6.0	6.6
0.3	1.2	2.4	3.6	4.9	6.1	7.3	8.5	9.7	10.9	12.2
0.4	1.9	3.7	5.6	7.5	9.4	11.2	13.1	15.0	16.8	18.7
0.5	2.6	5.2	7.8	10.5	13.1	15.7	18.3	20.9	23.5	26.2
0.6	3.4	6.9	10.3	13.8	17.2	20.6	24.1	27.5	31.0	34.4
0.7	4.3	8.7	13.0	17.3	21.7	26.0	30.3	34.7	39.0	43.3
0.8	5.3	10.6	15.9	21.2	26.5	31.8	37.1	42.4	47.7	53.0
0.9	6.3	12.6	19.0	25.3	31.6	37.9	44.2	50.5	56.9	63.2
1.0	7.4	14.8	22.2	29.6	37.0	44.4	51.8	59.2	66.6	74.0
1.1	8.5	17.1	25.6	34.1	42.7	51.2	59.8	68.3	76.8	85.4
1.2	9.7	19.5	29.2	38.9	48.6	58.4	68.1	77.8	87.5	97.3
1.3	11.0	21.9	32.9	43.9	54.8	65.8	76.8	87.7	98.7	110
1.4	12.3	24.5	36.8	49.0	61.3	73.5	85.8	98.1	110	123
1.5	13.6	27.2	40.8	54.4	68.0	81.6	95.2	109	122	136
1.6	15.0	30.0	44.9	59.9	74.9	89.9	105	120	135	150
1.7	16.4	32.8	49.2	65.6	82.0	98.4	115	131	148	164
1.8	17.9	35.7	53.6	71.5	89.4	107	125	143	161	179
1.9	19.4	38.8	58.1	77.5	96.9	116	136	155	174	194
2.0	20.9	41.9	62.8	83.7	105	126	147	167	188	209
2.1	22.5	45.0	67.6	90.1	113	135	158	180	203	225
2.2	24.1	48.3	72.4	96.6	121	145	169	193	217	241
2.3	25.8	51.6	77.4	103	129	155	181	206	232	258
2.4	27.5	55.0	82.5	110	138	165	193	220	248	275
2.5	29.3	58.5	87.8	117	146	176	205	234	263	293
2.6	31.0	62.0	93.1	124	155	186	217	248	279	310
2.7	32.8	65.7	98.5	131	164	197	230	263	295	328
2.8	34.7	69.3	104	139	173	208	243	277	312	347
2.9	36.5	73.1	110	146	183	219	256	292	329	365
3.0	38.5	76.9	115	154	192	231	269	308	346	385
3.1	40.4	80.8	121	162	202	242	283	323	364	404
3.2	42.4	84.7	127	169	212	254	297	339	381	424
3.3	44.4	88.7	133	177	222	266	311	355	399	444
3.4	46.4	92.8	139	186	232	278	325	371	418	464
3.5	48.5	96.9	145	194	242	291	339	388	436	485
3.6	50.5	101	152	202	253	303	354	404	455	505
3.7	52.7	105	158	211	263	316	369	421	474	527
3.8	54.8	110	164	219	274	329	384	439	493	548
3.9	57.0	114	171	228	285	342	399	456	513	570
4.0	59.2	118	178	237	296	355	414	474	533	592
4.1	61.4	123	184	246	307	369	430	491	553	614
4.2	63.7	127	191	255	318	382	446	510	573	637
4.3	66.0	132	198	264	330	396	462	528	594	660
4.4	68.3	137	205	273	341	410	478	546	615	683
4.5	70.6	141	212	283	353	424	494	565	636	706
4.6	73.0	146	219	292	365	438	511	584	657	730
4.7	75.4	151	226	302	377	452	528	603	679	754
4.8	77.8	156	233	311	389	467	545	623	700	778
4.9	80.3	161	241	321	401	482	562	642	722	803
5.0	82.7	165	248	331	414	496	579	662	745	827

11.8 Design Discharges (cfs) for Broad-Crested Rectangular Weirs ($C = 3.7$) (continued)

Head ft	Spillway Width—ft									
	2	4	6	8	10	12	14	16	18	20
5.1	85	170	256	341	426	511	597	682	767	852
5.2	88	175	263	351	439	526	614	702	790	877
5.3	90	181	271	361	451	542	632	722	813	903
5.4	93	186	279	371	464	557	650	743	836	929
5.5	95	191	286	382	477	573	668	764	859	954
5.6	98	196	294	392	490	588	686	785	883	981
5.7	101	201	302	403	504	604	705	806	906	1007
5.8	103	207	310	413	517	620	724	827	930	1034
5.9	106	212	318	424	530	636	742	848	954	1060
6.0	109	218	326	435	544	653	761	870	979	1088
6.1	111	223	334	446	557	669	780	892	1003	1115
6.2	114	228	343	457	571	685	800	914	1028	1142
6.3	117	234	351	468	585	702	819	936	1053	1170
6.4	120	240	359	479	599	719	839	958	1078	1198
6.5	123	245	368	491	613	736	858	981	1104	1226
6.6	125	251	376	502	627	753	878	1004	1129	1255
6.7	128	257	385	513	642	770	898	1027	1155	1283
6.8	131	262	394	525	656	787	919	1050	1181	1312
6.9	134	268	402	536	671	805	939	1073	1207	1341
7.0	137	274	411	548	685	822	959	1096	1233	1370
7.1	140	280	420	560	700	840	980	1120	1260	1400
7.2	143	286	429	572	715	858	1001	1144	1287	1430
7.3	146	292	438	584	730	876	1022	1168	1314	1460
7.4	149	298	447	596	745	894	1043	1192	1341	1490
7.5	152	304	456	608	760	912	1064	1216	1368	1520
7.6	155	310	465	620	775	930	1085	1240	1395	1550
7.7	158	316	474	632	791	949	1107	1265	1423	1581
7.8	161	322	484	645	806	967	1128	1290	1451	1612
7.9	164	329	493	657	822	986	1150	1315	1479	1643
8.0	167	335	502	670	837	1005	1172	1340	1507	1674
8.1	171	341	512	682	853	1024	1194	1365	1535	1706
8.2	174	348	521	695	869	1043	1216	1390	1564	1738
8.3	177	354	531	708	885	1062	1239	1416	1593	1769
8.4	180	360	540	721	901	1081	1261	1441	1621	1802
8.5	183	367	550	734	917	1100	1284	1467	1650	1834
8.6	187	373	560	747	933	1120	1306	1493	1680	1866
8.7	190	380	570	760	949	1139	1329	1519	1709	1899
8.8	193	386	580	773	966	1159	1352	1545	1739	1932
8.9	196	393	589	786	982	1179	1375	1572	1768	1965
9.0	200	400	599	799	999	1199	1399	1598	1798	1998
9.1	203	406	609	813	1016	1219	1422	1625	1828	2031
9.2	206	413	619	826	1032	1239	1445	1652	1858	2065
9.3	210	420	630	839	1049	1259	1469	1679	1889	2099
9.4	213	427	640	853	1066	1280	1493	1706	1919	2133
9.5	217	433	650	867	1083	1300	1517	1733	1950	2167
9.6	220	440	660	880	1101	1321	1541	1761	1981	2201
9.7	224	447	671	894	1118	1341	1565	1788	2012	2236
9.8	227	454	681	908	1135	1362	1589	1816	2043	2270
9.9	231	461	692	922	1153	1383	1614	1844	2075	2305
10.0	234	468	702	936	1170	1404	1638	1872	2106	2340

11.9 Discharge Values for Trickle Tubes of Corrugated Metal Pipe

Total Head* ft	Ratio of Barrel Diameter to Riser Diameter—*in.*					
	6:8	8:10	10:12	12:15	15:21	18:24
	cfs					
6	0.85	1.73	3.1	5.1	8.8	14.1
8	0.90	1.85	3.3	5.4	9.4	15.0
10	0.94	1.96	3.5	5.7	9.9	15.9
12	0.98	2.07	3.7	6.0	10.4	16.7
14	1.02	2.15	3.8	6.2	10.8	17.5
16	1.05	2.21	3.9	6.4	11.1	18.1
18	1.07	2.26	4.0	6.6	11.4	18.6
20	1.09	2.30	4.1	6.7	11.7	18.9
22	1.11	2.34	4.2	6.8	11.9	19.3
24	1.12	2.37	4.2	6.9	12.1	19.6
26	1.13	2.40	4.3	7.0	12.3	19.9

*Total head is measured as the vertical distance between a point 1.0 ft above the riser crest and the centerline of the barrel at its outlet end.

11.10 Velocity-Head Equation

Water velocity is computed from velocity-head measurements using:

$$v = \sqrt{2gh}$$

Where: v = velocity, ft/s
g = gravitational constant, ft/s²
h = velocity head, ft.

or:

v = velocity, m/s
g = gravitational constant, m/s²
h = velocity head, m.

Values of 32.1422 ft/s² and 9.79695 m/s² are used for g in the following tables.

11.11 Velocity–Head Relationship

Head	Velocity—ft/s									
ft	0.00	0.01	0.02	0.03	0.04	0.05	0.06	0.07	0.08	0.09
0.0	0.00	0.80	1.13	1.39	1.60	1.79	1.96	2.12	2.27	2.41
0.1	2.54	2.66	2.78	2.89	3.00	3.11	3.21	3.31	3.40	3.49
0.2	3.59	3.67	3.76	3.85	3.93	4.01	4.09	4.17	4.24	4.32
0.3	4.39	4.46	4.54	4.61	4.68	4.74	4.81	4.88	4.94	5.01
0.4	5.07	5.13	5.20	5.26	5.32	5.38	5.44	5.50	5.55	5.61
0.5	5.67	5.73	5.78	5.84	5.89	5.95	6.00	6.05	6.11	6.16
0.6	6.21	6.26	6.31	6.36	6.41	6.46	6.51	6.56	6.61	6.66
0.7	6.71	6.76	6.80	6.85	6.90	6.94	6.99	7.04	7.08	7.13
0.8	7.17	7.22	7.26	7.30	7.35	7.39	7.44	7.48	7.52	7.56
0.9	7.61	7.65	7.69	7.73	7.77	7.81	7.86	7.90	7.94	7.98
1.0	8.02	8.06	8.10	8.14	8.18	8.22	8.25	8.29	8.33	8.37
1.1	8.41	8.45	8.49	8.52	8.56	8.60	8.64	8.67	8.71	8.75
1.2	8.78	8.82	8.86	8.89	8.93	8.96	9.00	9.04	9.07	9.11
1.3	9.14	9.18	9.21	9.25	9.28	9.32	9.35	9.38	9.42	9.45
1.4	9.49	9.52	9.55	9.59	9.62	9.65	9.69	9.72	9.75	9.79
1.5	9.82	9.85	9.88	9.92	9.95	9.98	10.01	10.05	10.08	10.11
1.6	10.14	10.17	10.20	10.24	10.27	10.30	10.33	10.36	10.39	10.42
1.7	10.45	10.48	10.52	10.55	10.58	10.61	10.64	10.67	10.70	10.73
1.8	10.76	10.79	10.82	10.85	10.88	10.91	10.93	10.96	10.99	11.02
1.9	11.05	11.08	11.11	11.14	11.17	11.20	11.22	11.25	11.28	11.31
2.0	11.34	11.37	11.40	11.42	11.45	11.48	11.51	11.54	11.56	11.59
2.1	11.62	11.65	11.67	11.70	11.73	11.76	11.78	11.81	11.84	11.87
2.2	11.89	11.92	11.95	11.97	12.00	12.03	12.05	12.08	12.11	12.13
2.3	12.16	12.19	12.21	12.24	12.26	12.29	12.32	12.34	12.37	12.40
2.4	12.42	12.45	12.47	12.50	12.52	12.55	12.58	12.60	12.63	12.65
2.5	12.68	12.70	12.73	12.75	12.78	12.80	12.83	12.85	12.88	12.90
2.6	12.93	12.95	12.98	13.00	13.03	13.05	13.08	13.10	13.13	13.15
2.7	13.17	13.20	13.22	13.25	13.27	13.30	13.32	13.34	13.37	13.39
2.8	13.42	13.44	13.46	13.49	13.51	13.54	13.56	13.58	13.61	13.63
2.9	13.65	13.68	13.70	13.72	13.75	13.77	13.79	13.82	13.84	13.86
3.0	13.89	13.91	13.93	13.96	13.98	14.00	14.03	14.05	14.07	14.09
3.1	14.12	14.14	14.16	14.18	14.21	14.23	14.25	14.28	14.30	14.32
3.2	14.34	14.36	14.39	14.41	14.43	14.45	14.48	14.50	14.52	14.54
3.3	14.56	14.59	14.61	14.63	14.65	14.67	14.70	14.72	14.74	14.76
3.4	14.78	14.81	14.83	14.85	14.87	14.89	14.91	14.94	14.96	14.98
3.5	15.00	15.02	15.04	15.06	15.09	15.11	15.13	15.15	15.17	15.19
3.6	15.21	15.23	15.25	15.28	15.30	15.32	15.34	15.36	15.38	15.40
3.7	15.42	15.44	15.46	15.48	15.51	15.53	15.55	15.57	15.59	15.61
3.8	15.63	15.65	15.67	15.69	15.71	15.73	15.75	15.77	15.79	15.81
3.9	15.83	15.85	15.87	15.89	15.91	15.93	15.96	15.98	16.00	16.02
4.0	16.04	16.06	16.08	16.10	16.12	16.14	16.16	16.18	16.20	16.21
4.1	16.23	16.25	16.27	16.29	16.31	16.33	16.35	16.37	16.39	16.41
4.2	16.43	16.45	16.47	16.49	16.51	16.53	16.55	16.57	16.59	16.61
4.3	16.63	16.65	16.66	16.68	16.70	16.72	16.74	16.76	16.78	16.80
4.4	16.82	16.84	16.86	16.88	16.89	16.91	16.93	16.95	16.97	16.99
4.5	17.01	17.03	17.05	17.06	17.08	17.10	17.12	17.14	17.16	17.18
4.6	17.20	17.21	17.23	17.25	17.27	17.29	17.31	17.33	17.35	17.36
4.7	17.38	17.40	17.42	17.44	17.46	17.47	17.49	17.51	17.53	17.55
4.8	17.57	17.58	17.60	17.62	17.64	17.66	17.68	17.69	17.71	17.73
4.9	17.75	17.77	17.78	17.80	17.82	17.84	17.86	17.87	17.89	17.91

11.11　Velocity–Head Relationship (continued)

Head	Velocity—ft/s									
ft	0.00	0.01	0.02	0.03	0.04	0.05	0.06	0.07	0.08	0.09
5.0	17.93	17.95	17.96	17.98	18.00	18.02	18.04	18.05	18.07	18.09
5.1	18.11	18.12	18.14	18.16	18.18	18.20	18.21	18.23	18.25	18.27
5.2	18.28	18.30	18.32	18.34	18.35	18.37	18.39	18.41	18.42	18.44
5.3	18.46	18.48	18.49	18.51	18.53	18.55	18.56	18.58	18.60	18.61
5.4	18.63	18.65	18.67	18.68	18.70	18.72	18.73	18.75	18.77	18.79
5.5	18.80	18.82	18.84	18.85	18.87	18.89	18.91	18.92	18.94	18.96
5.6	18.97	18.99	19.01	19.02	19.04	19.06	19.07	19.09	19.11	19.13
5.7	19.14	19.16	19.18	19.19	19.21	19.23	19.24	19.26	19.28	19.29
5.8	19.31	19.33	19.34	19.36	19.38	19.39	19.41	19.43	19.44	19.46
5.9	19.48	19.49	19.51	19.52	19.54	19.56	19.57	19.59	19.61	19.62
6.0	19.64	19.66	19.67	19.69	19.70	19.72	19.74	19.75	19.77	19.79
6.1	19.80	19.82	19.83	19.85	19.87	19.88	19.90	19.92	19.93	19.95
6.2	19.96	19.98	20.00	20.01	20.03	20.04	20.06	20.08	20.09	20.11
6.3	20.12	20.14	20.16	20.17	20.19	20.20	20.22	20.24	20.25	20.27
6.4	20.28	20.30	20.32	20.33	20.35	20.36	20.38	20.39	20.41	20.43
6.5	20.44	20.46	20.47	20.49	20.50	20.52	20.54	20.55	20.57	20.58
6.6	20.60	20.61	20.63	20.64	20.66	20.68	20.69	20.71	20.72	20.74
6.7	20.75	20.77	20.78	20.80	20.82	20.83	20.85	20.86	20.88	20.89
6.8	20.91	20.92	20.94	20.95	20.97	20.98	21.00	21.02	21.03	21.05
6.9	21.06	21.08	21.09	21.11	21.12	21.14	21.15	21.17	21.18	21.20
7.0	21.21	21.23	21.24	21.26	21.27	21.29	21.30	21.32	21.33	21.35
7.1	21.36	21.38	21.39	21.41	21.42	21.44	21.45	21.47	21.48	21.50
7.2	21.51	21.53	21.54	21.56	21.57	21.59	21.60	21.62	21.63	21.65
7.3	21.66	21.68	21.69	21.71	21.72	21.74	21.75	21.77	21.78	21.80
7.4	21.81	21.83	21.84	21.85	21.87	21.88	21.90	21.91	21.93	21.94
7.5	21.96	21.97	21.99	22.00	22.02	22.03	22.05	22.06	22.07	22.09
7.6	22.10	22.12	22.13	22.15	22.16	22.18	22.19	22.20	22.22	22.23
7.7	22.25	22.26	22.28	22.29	22.31	22.32	22.33	22.35	22.36	22.38
7.8	22.39	22.41	22.42	22.44	22.45	22.46	22.48	22.49	22.51	22.52
7.9	22.54	22.55	22.56	22.58	22.59	22.61	22.62	22.64	22.65	22.66
8.0	22.68	22.69	22.71	22.72	22.73	22.75	22.76	22.78	22.79	22.80
8.1	22.82	22.83	22.85	22.86	22.88	22.89	22.90	22.92	22.93	22.95
8.2	22.96	22.97	22.99	23.00	23.02	23.03	23.04	23.06	23.07	23.09
8.3	23.10	23.11	23.13	23.14	23.15	23.17	23.18	23.20	23.21	23.22
8.4	23.24	23.25	23.27	23.28	23.29	23.31	23.32	23.33	23.35	23.36
8.5	23.38	23.39	23.40	23.42	23.43	23.44	23.46	23.47	23.49	23.50
8.6	23.51	23.53	23.54	23.55	23.57	23.58	23.59	23.61	23.62	23.64
8.7	23.65	23.66	23.68	23.69	23.70	23.72	23.73	23.74	23.76	23.77
8.8	23.78	23.80	23.81	23.83	23.84	23.85	23.87	23.88	23.89	23.91
8.9	23.92	23.93	23.95	23.96	23.97	23.99	24.00	24.01	24.03	24.04
9.0	24.05	24.07	24.08	24.09	24.11	24.12	24.13	24.15	24.16	24.17
9.1	24.19	24.20	24.21	24.23	24.24	24.25	24.27	24.28	24.29	24.31
9.2	24.32	24.33	24.35	24.36	24.37	24.39	24.40	24.41	24.42	24.44
9.3	24.45	24.46	24.48	24.49	24.50	24.52	24.53	24.54	24.56	24.57
9.4	24.58	24.60	24.61	24.62	24.63	24.65	24.66	24.67	24.69	24.70
9.5	24.71	24.73	24.74	24.75	24.76	24.78	24.79	24.80	24.82	24.83
9.6	24.84	24.86	24.87	24.88	24.89	24.91	24.92	24.93	24.95	24.96
9.7	24.97	24.98	25.00	25.01	25.02	25.04	25.05	25.06	25.07	25.09
9.8	25.10	25.11	25.13	25.14	25.15	25.16	25.18	25.19	25.20	25.21
9.9	25.23	25.24	25.25	25.27	25.28	25.29	25.30	25.32	25.33	25.34

11.12 Metric Velocity–Head Relationship

Head m	Velocity—m/s									
	0.00	0.01	0.02	0.03	0.04	0.05	0.06	0.07	0.08	0.09
0.0	0.00	0.44	0.63	0.77	0.89	0.99	1.08	1.17	1.25	1.33
0.1	1.40	1.47	1.53	1.60	1.66	1.71	1.77	1.83	1.88	1.93
0.2	1.98	2.03	2.08	2.12	2.17	2.21	2.26	2.30	2.34	2.38
0.3	2.42	2.46	2.50	2.54	2.58	2.62	2.66	2.69	2.73	2.76
0.4	2.80	2.83	2.87	2.90	2.94	2.97	3.00	3.03	3.07	3.10
0.5	3.13	3.16	3.19	3.22	3.25	3.28	3.31	3.34	3.37	3.40
0.6	3.43	3.46	3.49	3.51	3.54	3.57	3.60	3.62	3.65	3.68
0.7	3.70	3.73	3.76	3.78	3.81	3.83	3.86	3.88	3.91	3.93
0.8	3.96	3.98	4.01	4.03	4.06	4.08	4.10	4.13	4.15	4.18
0.9	4.20	4.22	4.25	4.27	4.29	4.31	4.34	4.36	4.38	4.40
1.0	4.43	4.45	4.47	4.49	4.51	4.54	4.56	4.58	4.60	4.62
1.1	4.64	4.66	4.68	4.71	4.73	4.75	4.77	4.79	4.81	4.83
1.2	4.85	4.87	4.89	4.91	4.93	4.95	4.97	4.99	5.01	5.03
1.3	5.05	5.07	5.09	5.10	5.12	5.14	5.16	5.18	5.20	5.22
1.4	5.24	5.26	5.27	5.29	5.31	5.33	5.35	5.37	5.39	5.40
1.5	5.42	5.44	5.46	5.48	5.49	5.51	5.53	5.55	5.56	5.58
1.6	5.60	5.62	5.63	5.65	5.67	5.69	5.70	5.72	5.74	5.75
1.7	5.77	5.79	5.81	5.82	5.84	5.86	5.87	5.89	5.91	5.92
1.8	5.94	5.96	5.97	5.99	6.00	6.02	6.04	6.05	6.07	6.09
1.9	6.10	6.12	6.13	6.15	6.17	6.18	6.20	6.21	6.23	6.24
2.0	6.26	6.28	6.29	6.31	6.32	6.34	6.35	6.37	6.38	6.40
2.1	6.41	6.43	6.45	6.46	6.48	6.49	6.51	6.52	6.54	6.55
2.2	6.57	6.58	6.60	6.61	6.62	6.64	6.65	6.67	6.68	6.70
2.3	6.71	6.73	6.74	6.76	6.77	6.79	6.80	6.81	6.83	6.84
2.4	6.86	6.87	6.89	6.90	6.91	6.93	6.94	6.96	6.97	6.98
2.5	7.00	7.01	7.03	7.04	7.05	7.07	7.08	7.10	7.11	7.12
2.6	7.14	7.15	7.16	7.18	7.19	7.21	7.22	7.23	7.25	7.26
2.7	7.27	7.29	7.30	7.31	7.33	7.34	7.35	7.37	7.38	7.39
2.8	7.41	7.42	7.43	7.45	7.46	7.47	7.49	7.50	7.51	7.53
2.9	7.54	7.55	7.56	7.58	7.59	7.60	7.62	7.63	7.64	7.65
3.0	7.67	7.68	7.69	7.71	7.72	7.73	7.74	7.76	7.77	7.78
3.1	7.79	7.81	7.82	7.83	7.84	7.86	7.87	7.88	7.89	7.91
3.2	7.92	7.93	7.94	7.96	7.97	7.98	7.99	8.00	8.02	8.03
3.3	8.04	8.05	8.07	8.08	8.09	8.10	8.11	8.13	8.14	8.15
3.4	8.16	8.17	8.19	8.20	8.21	8.22	8.23	8.25	8.26	8.27
3.5	8.28	8.29	8.30	8.32	8.33	8.34	8.35	8.36	8.38	8.39
3.6	8.40	8.41	8.42	8.43	8.45	8.46	8.47	8.48	8.49	8.50
3.7	8.51	8.53	8.54	8.55	8.56	8.57	8.58	8.59	8.61	8.62
3.8	8.63	8.64	8.65	8.66	8.67	8.69	8.70	8.71	8.72	8.73
3.9	8.74	8.75	8.76	8.78	8.79	8.80	8.81	8.82	8.83	8.84
4.0	8.85	8.86	8.88	8.89	8.90	8.91	8.92	8.93	8.94	8.95
4.1	8.96	8.97	8.98	9.00	9.01	9.02	9.03	9.04	9.05	9.06
4.2	9.07	9.08	9.09	9.10	9.11	9.13	9.14	9.15	9.16	9.17
4.3	9.18	9.19	9.20	9.21	9.22	9.23	9.24	9.25	9.26	9.27
4.4	9.29	9.30	9.31	9.32	9.33	9.34	9.35	9.36	9.37	9.38
4.5	9.39	9.40	9.41	9.42	9.43	9.44	9.45	9.46	9.47	9.48
4.6	9.49	9.50	9.51	9.52	9.53	9.55	9.56	9.57	9.58	9.59
4.7	9.60	9.61	9.62	9.63	9.64	9.65	9.66	9.67	9.68	9.69
4.8	9.70	9.71	9.72	9.73	9.74	9.75	9.76	9.77	9.78	9.79
4.9	9.80	9.81	9.82	9.83	9.84	9.85	9.86	9.87	9.88	9.89

11.13   Head–Pressure Relationships for Water at 10°C

Head	Pressure			
ft	$lb/in.^2$	lb/ft^2	kg/cm^2	kg/m^2
1	0.43	62.41	0.03	304.71
2	0.87	124.82	0.06	609.42
3	1.30	187.23	0.09	914.13
4	1.73	249.64	0.12	1218.84
5	2.17	312.05	0.15	1523.54
6	2.60	374.46	0.18	1828.25
7	3.03	436.87	0.21	2132.96
8	3.47	499.27	0.24	2437.67
9	3.90	561.68	0.27	2742.38
10	4.33	624.09	0.30	3047.09
11	4.77	686.50	0.34	3351.80
12	5.20	748.91	0.37	3656.51
13	5.63	811.32	0.40	3961.21
14	6.07	873.73	0.43	4265.92
15	6.50	936.14	0.46	4570.63
16	6.93	998.55	0.49	4875.34
17	7.37	1060.96	0.52	5180.05
18	7.80	1123.37	0.55	5484.76
19	8.23	1185.78	0.58	5789.47
20	8.67	1248.19	0.61	6094.18
21	9.10	1310.60	0.64	6398.89
22	9.53	1373.00	0.67	6703.59
23	9.97	1435.41	0.70	7008.30
24	10.40	1497.82	0.73	7313.01
25	10.83	1560.23	0.76	7617.72
26	11.27	1622.64	0.79	7922.43
27	11.70	1685.05	0.82	8227.14
28	12.14	1747.46	0.85	8531.85
29	12.57	1809.87	0.88	8836.56
30	13.00	1872.28	0.91	9141.27
31	13.44	1934.69	0.94	9445.97
32	13.87	1997.10	0.98	9750.68
33	14.30	2059.51	1.01	10 055.39
34	14.74	2121.92	1.04	10 360.10
35	15.17	2184.33	1.07	10 664.81
36	15.60	2246.73	1.10	10 969.52
37	16.04	2309.14	1.13	11 274.23
38	16.47	2371.55	1.16	11 578.94
39	16.90	2433.96	1.19	11 883.64
40	17.34	2496.37	1.22	12 188.35
41	17.77	2558.78	1.25	12 493.06
42	18.20	2621.19	1.28	12 797.77
43	18.64	2683.60	1.31	13 102.48
44	19.07	2746.01	1.34	13 407.19
45	19.50	2808.42	1.37	13 711.90
46	19.94	2870.83	1.40	14 016.61
47	20.37	2933.24	1.43	14 321.32
48	20.80	2995.65	1.46	14 626.02
49	21.24	3058.06	1.49	14 930.73
50	21.67	3120.46	1.52	15 235.44

11.13   Head–Pressure Relationships for Water at 10°C (continued)

Head	Pressure			
ft	lb/in.²	lb/ft²	kg/cm²	kg/m²
51	22.10	3182.87	1.55	15 540.15
52	22.54	3245.28	1.58	15 844.86
53	22.97	3307.69	1.61	16 149.57
54	23.40	3370.10	1.65	16 454.28
55	23.84	3432.51	1.68	16 758.99
56	24.27	3494.92	1.71	17 063.70
57	24.70	3557.33	1.74	17 368.40
58	25.14	3619.74	1.77	17 673.11
59	25.57	3682.15	1.80	17 977.82
60	26.00	3744.56	1.83	18 282.53
61	26.44	3806.97	1.86	18 587.24
62	26.87	3869.38	1.89	18 891.95
63	27.30	3931.79	1.92	19 196.66
64	27.74	3994.19	1.95	19 501.37
65	28.17	4056.60	1.98	19 806.07
66	28.60	4119.01	2.01	20 110.78
67	29.04	4181.42	2.04	20 415.49
68	29.47	4243.83	2.07	20 720.20
69	29.90	4306.24	2.10	21 024.91
70	30.34	4368.65	2.13	21 329.62
71	30.77	4431.06	2.16	21 634.33
72	31.20	4493.47	2.19	21 939.04
73	31.64	4555.88	2.22	22 243.75
74	32.07	4618.29	2.25	22 548.45
75	32.50	4680.70	2.29	22 853.16
76	32.94	4743.11	2.32	23 157.87
77	33.37	4805.52	2.35	23 462.58
78	33.81	4867.92	2.38	23 767.29
79	34.24	4930.33	2.41	24 072.00
80	34.67	4992.74	2.44	24 376.71
81	35.11	5055.15	2.47	24 681.42
82	35.54	5117.56	2.50	24 986.13
83	35.97	5179.97	2.53	25 290.83
84	36.41	5242.38	2.56	25 595.54
85	36.84	5304.79	2.59	25 900.25
86	37.27	5367.20	2.62	26 204.96
87	37.71	5429.61	2.65	26 509.67
88	38.14	5492.02	2.68	26 814.38
89	38.57	5554.43	2.71	27 119.09
90	39.01	5616.84	2.74	27 423.80
91	39.44	5679.25	2.77	27 728.50
92	39.87	5741.65	2.80	28 033.21
93	40.31	5804.06	2.83	28 337.92
94	40.74	5866.47	2.86	28 642.63
95	41.17	5928.88	2.89	28 947.34
96	41.61	5991.29	2.93	29 252.05
97	42.04	6053.70	2.96	29 556.76
98	42.47	6116.11	2.99	29 861.47
99	42.91	6178.52	3.02	30 166.18
100	43.34	6240.93	3.05	30 470.88

11.13 Head–Pressure Relationships for Water at 10°C (continued)

Head	Pressure			
ft	lb/in.²	lb/ft²	kg/cm²	kg/m²
101	43.77	6303.34	3.08	30 775.59
102	44.21	6365.75	3.11	31 080.30
103	44.64	6428.16	3.14	31 385.01
104	45.07	6490.57	3.17	31 689.72
105	45.51	6552.98	3.20	31 994.43
106	45.94	6615.38	3.23	32 299.14
107	46.37	6677.79	3.26	32 603.85
108	46.81	6740.20	3.29	32 908.55
109	47.24	6802.61	3.32	33 213.26
110	47.67	6865.02	3.35	33 517.97
111	48.11	6927.43	3.38	33 822.68
112	48.54	6989.84	3.41	34 127.39
113	48.97	7052.25	3.44	34 432.10
114	49.41	7114.66	3.47	34 736.81
115	49.84	7177.07	3.50	35 041.52
116	50.27	7239.48	3.53	35 346.23
117	50.71	7301.89	3.57	35 650.93
118	51.14	7364.30	3.60	35 955.64
119	51.57	7426.71	3.63	36 260.35
120	52.01	7489.11	3.66	36 565.06
121	52.44	7551.52	3.69	36 869.77
122	52.87	7613.93	3.72	37 174.48
123	53.31	7676.34	3.75	37 479.19
124	53.74	7738.75	3.78	37 783.90
125	54.17	7801.16	3.81	38 088.61
126	54.61	7863.57	3.84	38 393.31
127	55.04	7925.98	3.87	38 698.02
128	55.47	7988.39	3.90	39 002.73
129	55.91	8050.80	3.93	39 307.44
130	56.34	8113.21	3.96	39 612.15
131	56.78	8175.62	3.99	39 916.86
132	57.21	8238.03	4.02	40 221.57
133	57.64	8300.44	4.05	40 526.28
134	58.08	8362.84	4.08	40 830.98
135	58.51	8425.25	4.11	41 135.69
136	58.94	8487.66	4.14	41 440.40
137	59.38	8550.07	4.17	41 745.11
138	59.81	8612.48	4.20	42 049.82
139	60.24	8674.89	4.24	42 354.53
140	60.68	8737.30	4.27	42 659.24
141	61.11	8799.71	4.30	42 963.95
142	61.54	8862.12	4.33	43 268.66
143	61.98	8924.53	4.36	43 573.36
144	62.41	8986.94	4.39	43 878.07
145	62.84	9049.35	4.42	44 182.78
146	63.28	9111.76	4.45	44 487.49
147	63.71	9174.17	4.48	44 792.20
148	64.14	9236.57	4.51	45 096.91
149	64.58	9298.98	4.54	45 401.62
150	65.01	9361.39	4.57	45 706.33

11.13 Head–Pressure Relationships for Water at 10°C (continued)

Head	Pressure			
ft	lb/in.²	lb/ft²	kg/cm²	kg/m²
151	65.44	9423.80	4.60	46 011.04
152	65.88	9486.21	4.63	46 315.74
153	66.31	9548.62	4.66	46 620.45
154	66.74	9611.03	4.69	46 925.16
155	67.18	9673.44	4.72	47 229.87
156	67.61	9735.85	4.75	47 534.58
157	68.04	9798.26	4.78	47 839.29
158	68.48	9860.67	4.81	48 144.00
159	68.91	9923.08	4.84	48 448.71
160	69.34	9985.49	4.88	48 753.41
161	69.78	10 047.90	4.91	49 058.12
162	70.21	10 110.30	4.94	49 362.83
163	70.64	10 172.71	4.97	49 667.54
164	71.08	10 235.12	5.00	49 972.25
165	71.51	10 297.53	5.03	50 276.96
166	71.94	10 359.94	5.06	50 581.67
167	72.38	10 422.35	5.09	50 886.38
168	72.81	10 484.76	5.12	51 191.09
169	73.24	10 547.17	5.15	51 495.79
170	73.68	10 609.58	5.18	51 800.50
171	74.11	10 671.99	5.21	52 105.21
172	74.54	10 734.40	5.24	52 409.92
173	74.98	10 796.81	5.27	52 714.63
174	75.41	10 859.22	5.30	53 019.34
175	75.84	10 921.63	5.33	53 324.05
176	76.28	10 984.04	5.36	53 628.76
177	76.71	11 046.44	5.39	53 933.47
178	77.14	11 108.85	5.42	54 238.17
179	77.58	11 171.26	5.45	54 542.88
180	78.01	11 233.67	5.48	54 847.59
181	78.45	11 296.08	5.52	55 152.30
182	78.88	11 358.49	5.55	55 457.01
183	79.31	11 420.90	5.58	55 761.72
184	79.75	11 483.31	5.61	56 066.43
185	80.18	11 545.72	5.64	56 371.14
186	80.61	11 608.13	5.67	56 675.84
187	81.05	11 670.54	5.70	56 980.55
188	81.48	11 732.95	5.73	57 285.26
189	81.91	11 795.36	5.76	57 589.97
190	82.35	11 857.77	5.79	57 894.68
191	82.78	11 920.17	5.82	58 199.39
192	83.21	11 982.58	5.85	58 504.10
193	83.65	12 044.99	5.88	58 808.81
194	84.08	12 107.40	5.91	59 113.52
195	84.51	12 169.81	5.94	59 418.22
196	84.95	12 232.22	5.97	59 722.93
197	85.38	12 294.63	6.00	60 027.64
198	85.81	12 357.04	6.03	60 332.35
199	86.25	12 419.45	6.06	60 637.06
200	86.68	12 481.86	6.09	60 941.77

11.14   Manning Flow Equation _____

The Manning equation is expressed as:

$$v = \frac{1.486}{n} R^{2/3} S^{1/2}$$

Where: v = average velocity in the cross-section, ft/s
        R = the hydraulic radius, $A/$wp, ft
        A = cross-sectional area of wetted channel, ft²
       wp = wetted perimeter, ft
        S = water surface slope, ft/ft
        n = a roughness coefficient.

The Manning equation has wide application for computing flow in open channels. Values of the roughness coefficient, n, are given in the following tables for a variety of channel conditions. For computing $R^{2/3}$ and $S^{1/2}$, values of numbers to the two-thirds and one-half powers are given in Chapter 1, Mathematical Equivalents and Tables.

A nomograph is provided in Figure 8 for convenient solution of the Manning equation.

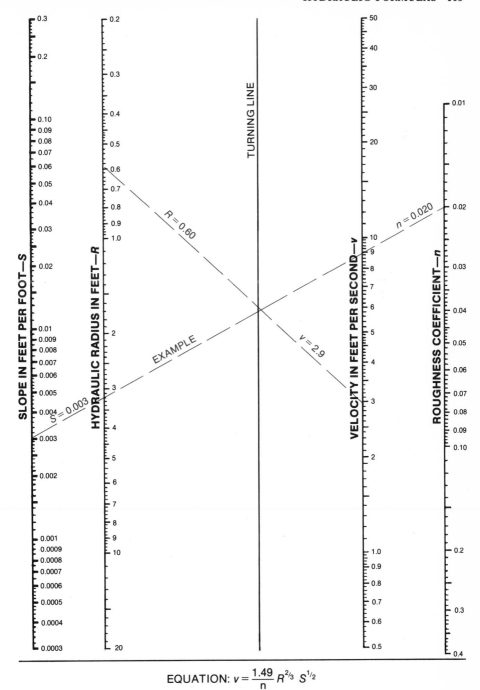

EQUATION: $v = \dfrac{1.49}{n} R^{2/3} S^{1/2}$

Figure 8   Nomograph for the Solution of the Manning Equation

11.15 Values of the Manning Roughness Coefficient, n

Description of Channel	Minimum	Normal	Maximum
A. Excavated or dredged			
1. Earth, straight and uniform			
a. Clean, recently completed	0.016	0.018	0.020
b. Clean, after weathering	0.018	0.022	0.025
c. Gravel, uniform section, clean	0.022	0.025	0.030
d. With short grass, few weeds	0.022	0.027	0.033
2. Earth, winding, sluggish			
a. No vegetation	0.023	0.025	0.030
b. Grass, some weeds	0.025	0.030	0.033
c. Dense weeds or aquatic plants in deep channels	0.030	0.035	0.040
d. Earth bottom and rubble sides	0.028	0.030	0.035
e. Stony bottom and weedy banks	0.025	0.035	0.040
f. Cobble bottom and clean sides	0.030	0.040	0.050
3. Dragline-excavated or dredged			
a. No vegetation	0.025	0.028	0.033
b. Light brush on banks	0.035	0.050	0.060
4. Rock cuts			
a. Smooth and uniform	0.025	0.035	0.040
b. Jagged and irregular	0.035	0.040	0.050
5. Channels not maintained, weeds and brush not cut			
a. Dense weeds as high as flow depth	0.050	0.080	0.120
b. Clean bottom, brush on sides	0.040	0.050	0.080
c. Same as above at highest stage of flow	0.045	0.070	0.110
d. Dense brush, high stage	0.080	0.100	0.140
B. Natural streams			
1. Minor streams with width at flood stage < 100 ft			
a. Streams on plains			
(1) Clean, straight, full stage no rifts or deep pools	0.025	0.030	0.033
(2) Same as above but more stones and weeds	0.030	0.035	0.040
(3) Clean, winding, some pools and bars	0.033	0.040	0.045
(4) Same as above but some weeds and stones	0.035	0.045	0.050
(5) Same as above but lower stages, more ineffective slopes and sections	0.040	0.048	0.055
(6) Same as (4) but more stones	0.045	0.050	0.060
(7) Sluggish reaches, weedy, deep pools	0.050	0.070	0.080
(8) Very weedy reaches, deep pools or floodways with heavy stand of timber and underbrush	0.075	0.100	0.150
b. Mountain streams, no vegetation in channel, banks usually steep, trees and brush along banks submerged at high stages			
(1) Bottom consists of gravels, cobbles, and few boulders	0.030	0.040	0.050
(2) Bottom consists of cobbles with large boulders	0.040	0.050	0.070
(3) Bottom consists of large boulders and some large organic debris, sinuous flow	0.050	0.070	0.100
2. Floodplains			
a. Pasture, no brush			
(1) Short grass	0.025	0.030	0.035
(2) High grass	0.030	0.035	0.050
b. Cultivated areas			
(1) No crop	0.020	0.030	0.040
(2) Mature row crops	0.025	0.035	0.045
(3) Mature field crops	0.030	0.040	0.050

11.15 Values of the Manning Roughness Coefficient, n (continued)

Description of Channel	Minimum	Normal	Maximum
c. Brush			
(1) Scattered brush, heavy weeds	0.035	0.050	0.070
(2) Light brush and trees in winter	0.035	0.050	0.060
(3) Light brush and trees in summer	0.040	0.060	0.080
(4) Medium to dense brush in winter	0.045	0.070	0.110
(5) Medium to dense brush in summer	0.070	0.100	0.160
d. Trees			
(1) Dense willows, summer, straight	0.110	0.150	0.200
(2) Cleared land, tree stumps no sprouts	0.030	0.040	0.050
(3) Same as above, with heavy sprout growth	0.050	0.060	0.080
(4) Heavy stand of timber, a few downed trees, little undergrowth, flood stage below branches	0.080	0.100	0.120
(5) Same as above, but with flood stage reaching branches	0.100	0.120	0.160
3. Major streams with width at flood stage > 100 ft			
a. Streams on plains			
(1) Sand channels	0.025	0.035	0.045
(2) Boulder channels	0.028	0.040	0.045
(3) Vegetation-lined channels at flood stage	0.045	—	0.120
b. Mountain streams			
(1) Cobbly bottom, no debris jams	0.028	0.035	0.040
(2) Cobbly bottom with debris jams	0.032	—	0.060
(3) Bottom with large boulders, no debris jams	0.045	0.050	0.070
(4) Bottom with large boulders, debris jams in channel	0.050	—	0.100
C. Channels in swales with vegetation			
1. Depth of flow up to 0.7 ft			
a. Bermuda grass, bluegrass, buffalo grass			
(1) Height 2–4 in.	0.045	—	0.060
(2) Height 4–6 in.	0.060	—	0.090
b. Good stand, any grass			
(1) Height 6–12 in.	0.060	—	0.180
(2) Height 12–24 in.	0.180	—	0.300
c. Fair stand, any grass			
(1) Height 6–12 in.	0.050	—	0.140
(2) Height 12–24 in.	0.140	—	0.250
2. Depth of flow 0.7–1.5 ft			
a. Bermuda grass, bluegrass, buffalo grass			
(1) Height 2–4 in.	0.035	—	0.055
(2) Height 4–6 in.	0.040	—	0.060
b. Good stand, any grass			
(1) Height 6–12 in.	0.050	—	0.120
(2) Height 12–24 in.	0.100	—	0.200
c. Fair stand, any grass			
(1) Height 6–12 in.	0.040	—	0.100
(2) Height 12–24 in.	0.080	—	0.170

12

Hydrologic and Edaphic Data

12.1   Sediment Yield Computations ————————————————————

Sediment discharge rate is computed as:

$$Q_s = Q_w C_s k$$

Where: Q_s = sediment discharge, tons/day
C_s = discharge-weighted mean concentration, mg/L
Q_w = mean daily streamflow rate, cfs
k = 0.0027.

Annual sediment yield over a drainage basin is computed as:

$$Q_s \text{ (annual)} = 365 \, Q_s/A$$

Where: Q_s = sediment discharge rate, tons/day
A = drainage area, acres
Q_s (annual) = annual sediment yield, tons/acre.

To convert tons/acre to acre-ft/mi^2 multiply by 0.3918.

12.2   Reservoir Sediment Densities

Dominant Grain Size	Permanently Submerged	Aerated
	lb/ft^3	
Clay	40–60	60–80
Silt	55–75	75–85
Clay-silt	40–65	65–85
Sand-silt	75–95	95–110
Clay-silt-sand	50–80	80–100
Sand	85–100	85–100
Gravel	85–125	85–125
Poorly sorted sand and gravel	95–130	95–130

12.3   Size Classes of Sediment Particles

Type of Sediment	Size Range	
	mm	*in.*
Clay	<0.004	<0.000 16
Silt	0.004–0.06	0.000 15–0.002 5
Very fine sand	0.06–0.10	0.002 5–0.004
Fine sand	0.10–0.25	0.004–0.010
Medium sand	0.25–0.50	0.010–0.020
Coarse sand	0.5–1.0	0.02–0.04
Very coarse sand	1.0–2.0	0.04–0.08
Gravel	2.0–64	0.08–2.5
Cobble	64–256	2.5–10
Boulder	256–4096	10–161

12.4   Sediment Delivery Ratios

The sediment delivery ratio is defined as the ratio of sediment yield from a basin to the total erosion occurring within the basin.

Information on sediment delivery ratios is scarce because of the difficulty and cost of collecting the necessary data.

Vanoni (1975) and Renfro (1975) have suggested relationships between sediment delivery ratio and drainage area. Figure 9 is based on their work. The relationship should be used with extreme caution and considerable judgment. For a given drainage area, the ratio will vary with (1) nature and location of the sediment source, (2) nature of the transport system, i.e., the runoff regime, (3) texture of eroded material, (4) location of depositional areas, and (5) watershed characteristics such as relief and slope, basin shape, and stream channel density.

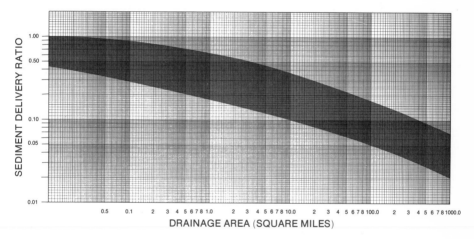

Figure 9   Sediment Delivery Ratio as a Function of Drainage Area

12.5   Factors for Converting Sediment Concentration in ppm to mg/L

Conc. Range ($ppm \times 10^3$)	Factor	Conc. Range ($ppm \times 10^3$)	Factor	Conc. Range ($ppm \times 10^3$)	Factor
0–15.9	1.00	160.0–185.0	1.12	301.0–321.0	1.24
16.0–46.8	1.02	186.0–210.0	1.14	322.0–341.0	1.26
46.9–76.5	1.04	211.0–233.0	1.16	342.0–361.0	1.28
76.6–105.0	1.06	234.0–256.0	1.18	362.0–380.0	1.30
106.0–133.0	1.08	257.0–279.0	1.20	381.0–399.0	1.32
134.0–159.0	1.10	280.0–300.0	1.22	400.0–416.0	1.34

12.6   Permeability of Geologic Materials

Permeability—*ft/day*										
10^5	10^4	10^3	10^2	10^1	1	10^{-1}	10^{-2}	10^{-3}	10^{-4}	10^{-5}
Clean gravel		Clean sand and sand and gravel		Fine sand		Silt, clay, and mix of sand, silt, and clay		Massive clay		
Vesicular/scoriaceous basalt and cavernous dolomite and limestone		Clean sandstone and fractured igneous and metamorphic rocks		Laminated sandstone, shale, mudstone		Massive igneous and metamorphic rocks				
10^5	10^4	10^3	10^2	10^1	1	10^{-1}	10^{-2}	10^{-3}	10^{-4}	10^{-5}

12.7   The Thompson Equation for Gully Advance

$$R = 0.15 \, A^{0.49} \, S^{0.14} \, P^{0.74} \, E^{1.00}$$

Where: R = average annual gully head advance, ft
A = drainage area, acres
S = slope of approach channel, percent
P = annual summation of rainfall from rains of 0.5 in. or more per 24 h, in.
E = clay content of eroding soil profile, percent-by-weight.

12.8   Spacing of Gully Check Dams

Heede (1976) recommends the following equation for determining the spacing of check dams:

$$S = \frac{H}{K \, G \cos \alpha}$$

Where: S = spacing, ft
H = effective dam height, measured from the gully bottom to spillway crest, ft
G = gully gradient, ft/ft
α = angle corresponding to gully gradient
K = a constant.

The value of K is determined locally from observing the gradient of sediment deposits, assumed to be $(1-K)G$. This equation is very helpful not only for designing a gully control project, but also for analyzing the cost tradeoffs between various dam spacings and various dam heights.

12.9   Riprap Sizing

Figure 10 may be used to size rock used for channel riprap, headcut control aprons, drainage channels, loose-rock check dams, culvert outflow energy dissipaters, and spillways.

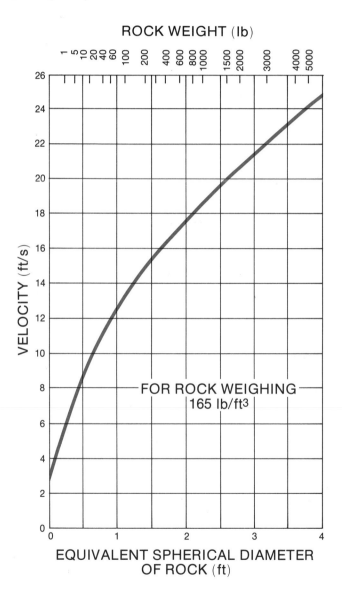

Figure 10   Recommended Riprap Sizes as a Function of Water Velocity

12.10   Maximum Flow Depth for Earthen Channels _____

Figure 11 may be used to determine the recommended maximum depth of flow for earthen channels used for spillways, road drainage facilities, grassed waterways prior to vegetation establishment, and similar applications.

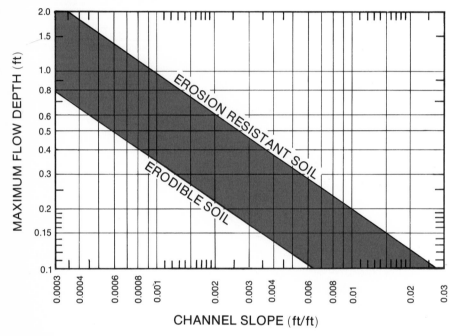

Figure 11   Maximum Permissible Depth of Flow for Bare Earthen Channels

12.11   Operational Procedures for Estimating Snowmelt Runoff _____

Although there have been more complex snowmelt models developed in recent years, models that relate snowmelt to an air temperature index have proven to be quite reliable for operational purposes, particularly when precipitation and air temperature are the only data available to the hydrologist.

The following relationships can be used to predict snowmelt for deep, continuous snowpacks in mountainous areas.

$$M = M_f (T_i - T_b)$$

Where: M = melt rate in inches of water per unit time
M_f = melt factor, in./°F/unit time
T_i = index air temperature, °F
T_b = base temperature, °F.

The index air temperature is usually either the maximum or the mean daily temperature. The base temperature is usually 32°F. The melt factor, M_f, is dependent on shortwave radiation, the transmission of radiation through the vegetation canopy, and the snow albedo. Melt factors should be developed for homogeneous portions of the watershed. In practice, clear-weather melt factors have ranged between 0.03 and 0.15 in. per °F per day when $T_b = 32$°F and $T_i =$ the mean daily air temperature. For periods of rain, the snowmelt equation is adjusted by adding a rainfall term as follows:

$$M = 0.007 \, P \, (T_i - T_b)$$

Where: M = melt rate, in./day
P = rainfall, in./day.

Gray (1970) gives the following convenient equations for total basin snowmelt during rain, accounting for forest cover effects:

For open and partly forested areas (0–60 percent cover):

$$M = (0.029 + 0.0084 \, k \, u_b + 0.007 \, P)(T_i - 32) + 0.09$$

For heavily forested areas (60–100 percent cover):

$$M = (0.074 + 0.007 \, P)(T_i - 32) + 0.05$$

Where: k = coefficient, which varies from 1.0 for the plains to 0.3 for forested areas
u_b = wind speed, mph, at 50-ft height.

12.12   Equations for Determining Mean Annual Runoff for Streams in the Western United States

The basic equation for mean annual flow (acre-ft/yr) using the channel geometry method of Hedman and Osterkamp (1982) is:

$$Q = a W^b$$

Where: a = a regression coefficient
W = active channel width, ft
b = a regression coefficient.

Values of a and b and the regions and channel characteristics to which they apply are given below:

Flow Frequency	Region	Percent Time*	Channel Material†	a	b	SE†‡
Perennial	Mountain	>80	sc, a	64.00	1.88	28
Intermittent	Plains north of 39N	10–80	sc, a	40.00	1.80	50
			s	40.00	1.65	50
	Plains south of 39N	10–80	sc, a	20.00	1.65	50
			s	20.00	1.55	50
Ephemeral	Plains and intermontane	6–9	sc, a	10.00	1.55	n/a
			s	10.00	1.50	n/a
		2–5	sc, a	4.00	1.50	40
			s	4.00	1.40	40
	Desert southwest	≤1	sc, a	0.04	1.75	75
			s	0.04	1.40	75

*Percent time refers to percent of time flow is present in the channel.
†sc = silt and clay; a = armored; s = sand; n/a = not available.
‡SE = standard error of estimate, in percent.

12.13   Equations for Determining Flood-frequency Discharge for Streams in the Western United States

The same basic equation as used for mean annual flow has been used by Hedman and Osterkamp (1982) for flood frequencies. Values of a and b and the regions to which they apply are given in the table at the top of the next page. The discharge, Q, is expressed in cfs.

Region	Return Period Years	a	b	SE
Alpine and pine-forested mountain	2	1.3	1.65	44
	5	2.8	1.60	37
	10	4.4	1.55	38
	25	7.0	1.50	42
	50	9.6	1.45	45
	100	13	1.40	50
Northern plains and intermontane areas east of	2	4.8	1.60	62
Rocky Mountains	5	24	1.40	42
	10	46	1.35	40
	25	61	1.30	44
	50	130	1.30	51
	100	160	1.25	58
Southern plains east of Rocky Mountains	2	7.8	1.70	66
	5	39	1.60	57
	10	84	1.55	56
	25	180	1.50	57
	50	270	1.50	59
	100	370	1.50	62
Plains and intermontane areas west of Rocky Mountains	2	1.8	1.70	120
	5	7	1.60	73
	10	14	1.50	60
	25	22	1.50	62
	50	44	1.40	71
	100	59	1.40	83

12.14   Grunsky's Rule for Mean Annual Runoff

Mean annual runoff can be estimated using the following equation:

$$Q = a P^2$$

Where: Q = annual runoff, in.
P = annual precipitation, in.
a = coefficient.

Values of a can be obtained from representative studies of precipitation-runoff relations or by using the following guidelines:

Characteristic	Value of a (0.00X) 3–6	7–9	10–15
Exposure	S, SW	W, E	N, E
Elevation	low	med	high
Summer rainfall	high	med	low
Temperature	high	med	low
Soil	porous	med	tight
Slopes	shallow	mod	steep

12.15   Runoff Curve Numbers For Use in The Soil Conservation Service's (1972) Runoff Modeling Procedure

Vegetation Type or Land Use	Treatment or Practice	Hydrologic Condition	Hydrologic Soil Group*			
			A	B	C	D
Grassland		Poor	66	79	86	89
		Fair	51	69	79	84
		Good	37	61	74	80
	Contoured	Poor	47	67	78	83
	Contoured	Fair	38	61	74	80
	Contoured	Good	28	55	70	77
Herbaceous		Poor	68	80	87	90
		Fair	55	71	81	85
		Good	42	63	74	81
Desert brush		Poor	68	80	87	90
		Fair	52	70	80	85
		Good	39	62	75	80
Sagebrush		Poor	47	67	78	83
		Fair	—	48	65	74
		Good	—	30	53	64
Pinyon-juniper		Poor	60	75	83	87
		Fair	34	58	73	78
		Good	—	41	61	70
Chaparral (Ariz.)		Poor	68	80	87	93
		Fair	32	57	71	83
		Good	—	41	58	74
Oak-aspen		Poor	43	64	76	82
		Fair	—	47	64	73
		Good	—	30	53	64
Ponderosa pine		Poor	45	66	77	83
		Fair	29	56	70	77
		Good	—	46	64	72
Forest		Poor	45	66	77	83
		Fair	36	60	73	79
		Good	25	55	70	77
Roads (dirt)		—	72	82	90	92
Bare rock		—	96	96	96	96
Water surfaces		—	100	100	100	100

NOTE: For the agricultural practices above, poor hydrologic condition means less than 20 percent and good hydrologic condition means more than 20 percent of the surface is covered with residue.
*See Table 12.16 for definitions of hydrologic soil groups.

12.15   Runoff Curve Numbers (continued)

Vegetation Type or Land Use	Treatment or Practice	Hydrologic Condition	Hydrologic Soil Group*			
			A	B	C	D
Mined lands	Contour furrowing	Max	26	57	70	78
	Contour furrowing	Min	47	67	81	88
	Imprinting	Max	30	58	71	78
	Imprinting	Min	47	67	81	88
	Pitting	Max	34	59	72	79
	Pitting	Min	57	73	83	88
	Ripping	Max	39	61	74	80
	Ripping	Min	68	79	86	89
Fallow	Straight row	—	77	86	91	94
	Straight row and conserv. tillage	Poor	75	84	89	92
	Straight row and conserv. tillage	Good	74	83	87	90
Row crops	Straight row	Poor	72	81	88	91
	Straight row	Good	67	78	85	89
	Straight row and conserv. tillage	Poor	71	79	86	89
	Straight row and conserv. tillage	Good	64	75	82	85
	Contoured	Poor	70	79	84	88
	Contoured	Good	65	75	82	86
	Contoured and conserv. tillage	Poor	69	78	83	87
	Contoured and conserv. tillage	Good	64	74	80	84
	Contoured and terraces	Poor	66	74	80	82
	Contoured and terraces	Good	62	71	78	81
	Contoured, terraces, and conserv. tillage	Poor	65	73	79	81
	Contoured, terraces, and conserv. tillage	Good	61	70	76	79
Small grains	Straight row	Poor	65	76	84	88
	Straight row	Good	63	75	83	87
	Straight row and conserv. tillage	Poor	64	74	82	86
	Straight row and conserv. tillage	Good	60	72	80	84
	Contoured	Poor	63	74	82	85
	Contoured	Good	61	73	81	84
	Contoured and conserv. tillage	Poor	62	73	81	84
	Contoured and conserv. tillage	Good	60	72	79	82
	Contoured and terraces	Poor	61	72	79	82
	Contoured and terraces	Good	59	70	78	81
	Contoured, terraces, and conserv. tillage	Poor	60	71	78	81
	Contoured, terraces, and conserv. tillage	Good	58	69	76	79

NOTE: For the agricultural practices above, poor hydrologic condition means less than 20 percent and good hydrologic condition means more than 20 percent of the surface is covered with residue.
*See Table 12.16 for definitions of hydrologic soil groups.

12.16   Hydrologic Soil Groups*

Group	Runoff Potential	Description
A	Low	Soils having high infiltration rates even when thoroughly wetted and consisting chiefly of deep, well to excessively drained sands or gravels. These soils have a high rate of water transmission.
B	Low-moderate	Soils having moderate infiltration rates when thoroughly wetted and consisting chiefly of moderately deep to deep, moderately well to well drained soils with moderately fine to moderately coarse textures. These soils have a moderate rate of water transmission.
C	Moderate-high	Soils having slow infiltration rates when thoroughly wetted and consisting chiefly of soils with a layer that impedes downward movement of water, or soils with moderately fine to fine texture. These soils have a slow rate of water transmission.
D	High	Soils having very slow infiltration rates when thoroughly wetted and consisting chiefly of clay soils with a high swelling potential, soils with a permanent high water table, soils with a claypan or clay layer at or near the surface, and shallow soils over nearly impervious material. These soils have a very slow rate of water transmission.

*As defined by the Soil Conservation Service (1972)

13

Basic Watershed Inventory Checklist

13.1 Basic Watershed Inventory Checklist _____

    I.   Watershed Name and Location
        A. Name of watershed
        B. Location
            1. County and state
            2. Tributary to
            3. Hydrologic Unit Code
        C. Watershed size

    II.   Watershed Characteristics
        A. Climate
            1. Precipitation
               a. Average annual
               b. Seasonal
               c. Growing season
               d. Snow accumulation
               e. Precipitation intensity-frequency
            2. Evapotranspiration loss
            3. Wind
               a. Prevailing direction
               b. Wind run
            4. Other pertinent climatic data
        B. Geology and physiography
            1. General descriptive geology
               a. History
               b. Structure
            2. Elevation and relief
               a. Maximum, minimum
               b. Hypsometric relations
            3. Slope and aspect
               a. Slope classes
               b. General and mean aspect
            4. Drainage features
               a. Drainage pattern: dendritic, radial, parallel, etc.
               b. Watershed shape factor
               c. Drainage density
                  (1) length of well-defined channel per unit area
                  (2) length of perennial flow channel per unit area
               d. Location and description of lakes, bogs, springs
            5. Parent rock: igneous, metamorphic, sedimentary, etc.

    C. Soils
       1. Soil type classification
       2. Hydrologic characteristics
         a. Soil depth
         b. Permeability classes
         c. Impermeable layers
         d. Soil erodibility
           (1) Wischmeier's K
           (2) Universal Soil Loss Equation
    D. Land use and cover conditions
       1. Distribution by classes
         a. Urban
         b. Agricultural
         c. Wildland (forest, range)
       2. Ownership patterns
         a. Federal, state, private
         b. Stability and trends
       3. Forest conditions (type and age, logging, fire)
       4. Range conditions (type, use, range condition/trend)
       5. Roads (type, use, condition, drainage)
       6. Recreational use

III. Watershed Hydrology
    A. Erosion conditions
       1. Upland areas
       2. Streambanks
       3. Roads
       4. Mass erosion (landslides, avalanche paths, etc.)
    B. Floods
       1. Frequency
       2. Season of year
       3. Expected maximum flows and their duration
       4. Flood damages
    C. Streamflow
       1. Source (lakes, springs, snowmelt, rain, etc.)
       2. Annual yield
       3. Seasonal
       4. Flow duration curve
       5. Minimum flows

D. Quality of water
   1. Turbidity, suspended sediment
   2. Total dissolved solids; principal ions, cations
   3. Bacterial
   4. Toxic metals
   5. Relationship to discharge

IV. Water Uses and Needs

V.   Water Problems Identified by Users

VI. Management Recommendations (to meet specific problems)
     A. Forest land
        1. Silvicultural
        2. Logging practices
        3. Road systems
     B. Range land
        1. Grazing management
        2. Range improvement and range rehabilitation
        3. Water developments
     C. Recreation
     D. Wildlife habitat management
     E. Riparian zone management
     F. Engineering systems (roads, trails, road crossings, etc.)
     G. Mineral exploration and extraction

VII. Summary of Inventory—Significant Findings

Bibliography

BRAKENSIEK, D.L., OSBORN, H.B., and RAWLS, W.J. (coordinators). Field Manual for Research in Agricultural Hydrology. USDA Agriculture Handbook 224 (1979).

BRATER, E.F. and KING, H.W. Handbook of Hydraulics. McGraw-Hill Book Co., New York (6th ed., 1976).

CHOW, V.T. (editor). Handbook of Applied Hydrology. McGraw-Hill Book Co., New York (1964).

Engineering Field Tables. US Dept. Agriculture, Forest Service and US Dept. Interior, Bureau of Land Management. USGPO (4th ed., 1976).

Factors for High-Precision Conversion: US Customary and Metric Units. US Dept. of Commerce. National Bureau of Standards. LC-1071 (1976).

HEDMAN, E.R. and OSTERKAMP, W.R. Streamflow Characteristics Related to Channel Geometry of Streams in Western United States. US Geological Survey Water-Supply Paper 2193 (1982).

HEEDE, B.H. Gully Development and Control: The Status of Our Knowledge. USDA Forest Service Research Paper RM-169 (1976).

HULSING, H. Measurement of Peak Discharge at Dams by Indirect Method. US Geological Survey Tech. of Water-Resources Invest., Book 3, Chapter A5 (1967).

LIST, R.J. Smithsonian Meteorological Tables. Smithsonian Institution Press, Washington, DC (6th ed., 1968).

Metric Manual. US Dept. Interior, Bureau of Reclamation. USGPO (1978).

Metric Practice. ASTM Standard E 380-79. American Society for Testing and Materials, Philadelphia, PA (1980).

MCCUEN, R.H. Statistical Terminology: Definitions and Interpretation for Flood Peak Estimation. Water Resources Bulletin 15(4):1106-1116 (1979).

National Engineering Handbook, Section 4, Hydrology. US Dept. Agriculture, Soil Conservation Service (1972).

PARMLEY, R.O. (editor). Field Engineer's Manual. McGraw-Hill Book Co., New York (1981).

RANTZ, S.E. Measurement and Computation of Streamflow: Volume 2. Computation of Discharge. US Geological Survey Water-Supply Paper 2175, pp. 285-631 (1982).

RAWLS, W.J. and RICHARDSON, H.H. Runoff Curve Numbers for Conservation Tillage. Jour. Soil and Water Conservation, Nov.-Dec. 1983, pp. 494-496 (1983).

RENFRO, G.W. Use of Erosion Equations and Sediment-Delivery Ratios for Predicting Sediment Yield. Present and Prospective Technology for Predicting Sediment Yields and Sources, USDA Agricultural Research Service Report ARS-S-40, pp. 34–35 (1975).

VANONI, V.A. (editor). Sedimentation Engineering. American Society of Civil Engineers, New York (1975).

Water Measurement Manual. US Dept. Interior, Bureau of Reclamation. USGPO (2nd ed., 1974).

Index